CANAL INC[
AND LIF[

CANAL INCLINES AND LIFTS

David Tew

ALAN SUTTON
1984

Alan Sutton Publishing Limited
Brunswick Road · Gloucester

First published 1984

British Library Cataloguing in Publication Data

Tew, David
    Canal inclines and lifts.
    1. Canal—Inclined planes   2. Canal Lifts
    I. Title
    627′.1353   TC763

    ISBN 0-86299-031-9

Typesetting and origination by
Alan Sutton Publishing Limited.
Printed in Great Britain.

CONTENTS

INTRODUCTION

This is a study of the various systems of lifts and inclines by which waterways have overcome changes in level since the commencement of inland navigation. In order to cover the subject as completely as possible other related matters have been touched upon, including the transporting of boats overland on rollers, and the 'ship railways' which have been operated in various places.

There have been many plans for lifts and inclines which have not yet been put into practice, and in general, however interesting in themselves, these have not been mentioned unless they help to explain later developments, or indicate the lines on which future schemes may be developed. For these reasons, the eighteenth-century proposals of Edmund Leach and the recent proposals of the German engineer L. Rothmund have been touched on.

Although in many cases the cost of installations is known, it seems so difficult to express it in terms which will convey any real meaning to the present day reader, that in general cost has not been considered.

Dimensions have where possible been given in metric terms unless English or American Canals are being dealt with.

PART I

CHAPTER I

INCLINES AND SIMILAR DEVICES
PRIOR TO 1750

The earliest device so far discovered for transporting boats or ships across
land, overcoming differences in levels, was in ancient Egypt at Mirgissa (20
kilometres south of Wadi Halfa) at the second cataract on the River Nile.
Here, the Nile could be navigated only during high water, at most between
the end of July and the end of November. For the rest of the year the rapids
north of Mirgissa were impassable for boats. Probably during the reign of
Amenemnes V of the XIII dynasty (*c.* 1700 BC) a slipway of Nile silt was
constructed about three or four kilometres long, between Mirgissa and
Abusir Rock; this was slightly curved in section, being lower in the middle,
with cross-pieces of wood every fifty centimetres or so. Nile silt has the
peculiarity that it is very slippery when wet, so that if, when a boat was on
the slipway, a man went in front pouring water on the slipway, experiments have shown that the difficulty would be in restraining the boat rather
than in dragging it along. As traces could still be seen of a keel of a boat on
the slipway it is probable that the boats themselves were pulled over the
slipway without their being put on a carriage for the purpose. Unfortunately the site is now covered by the waters of the Aswan High Dam.[1] The
purpose of this device for passing the rapids was presumably to enable
provisions to be taken to the forts of the cataract region, and stone from the
quarries of Upper Egypt to be taken to the cities of Lower Egypt.

In classical times boats were transported across the Isthmus of Corinth in
Greece on the *Diolkos*. This appears to have been a 'rutway' paved with
stone. How the ships were hauled over this is not absolutely certain: at one
time it was thought that they travelled on rollers, but since the discovery of
the remains of the 'rutway' it seems more likely that they were hauled over
the Isthmus on some sort of wheeled cradle. The *Diolkos* is said to have been
constructed in the time of Periander, tyrant of Corinth, who died in 585 BC
aged about eighty, and may have continued in use as late as the ninth
century AD.[2] It is interesting that Periander had Egyptian connections and
gave one of his sons an Egyptian-sounding name, so that he may have had
knowledge of the Egyptian device.

Chinese engineers appear to have devised means of transferring boats
(some of considerable size) from one level of a waterway to another with a
long haul overland.[3]

The earliest example of this is in the Magic Canal built by Shih Lu in 219 BC in which it appears that flash locks were used, but as early as AD 385 there were seven double slipways on the Ssu River section of the Grand Canal which was built by Hsieh Hsuan, a general and also a philosopher. Boats were hauled over these double inclines by capstans, worked either by ox-whims known as *chhien tai* or by large teams of men. According to records quoted by Dr. Needham, these double inclines fell out of favour about the eleventh century AD, and were replaced for a time by pound locks. Nevertheless, many foreign travellers writing of their experience in China mention such inclines. As early as AD 1073, Jojim, a Japanese monk, passed over a double slipway worked by winches near Hang-chow, and in AD 1307 Rashin al-Din, writing of the Grand Canal, wrote: 'vessels are hoisted up by means of machinery, whatever their size, and let down on the other side into the water'.[4]

In 1793 Sir John Barrow, a member of Lord Macartney's celebrated embassy, wrote:

> Thus, where canals are carried over surfaces that are too hilly and uneven to admit of one continued level, they descend from place to place, as it were, by steps, at each of which is an inclined plane; the height from the upper canal to the lower being generally from six to ten feet; and the angle of the plane being from 45° to 50°.
>
> All vessels navigating such canals must be hoisted up these planes by the assistance of upright capstans, without which it would scarcely be possible to get those of large dimensions, together with their cargo, out of one canal into the other; and they are gently lowered in the same manner. This awkward contrivance may perhaps less imply the ignorance of locks or other methods practised elsewhere, than the unwillingness of the government to suffer any innovation that might be the means of depriving many thousands of obtaining that scanty subsistence which they now derive from their attendance at these capstans.[5]

It was reported in the seventeenth century that these inclines were not in use on the Grand Canal for fear of damaging the very large Imperial Barques, but their use in China has certainly continued until modern times, the most recent illustration seen being in a book published in New York in 1934.[6]

In the Low Countries, devices known as *overdrach* or *ponts aux rouleaux* were constructed as early as the twelfth century, for use by boats of six to eight tons. At least four of these devices existed on the River Yser between Ypres and Nieuport.[7] A drawing from the Archives of Ypres shows a variety of these inclines clearly[8]: they were constructed with wooden planking and a counterslope at the top of the incline. In one design, at the top of the incline there was a roof from one side of the incline to the other with a horizontal bar across, and the boat was hauled up by a treadmill: in another design it was hauled up by a waterwheel. Other designs illustrated show a double incline and a boat being hauled up apparently by a windlass. Horse-gins were also used. It seems that boats were fitted with a chain at the stern; the cable used for hauling up the boat was fixed to this chain and also to the bow of the boat. An *overdrach* at Watten in the Pas de Calais existed until its destruction at the time of the siege of St. Omer in 1638.[9] There was a similar device near Amsterdam which lasted long enough to be photographed. Dr. Michel Goppel of Amsterdam has kindly written as follows:

> *'Overtoom'* (rhymes with home) is the generic name for the device for hauling ships, or rather small boats and barges from one waterway to another. It seems that in the fifteenth century Haarlem could only be reached from Amsterdam via a complicated set of waterways, and for a more direct connection a new canal was dug, and the water level difference was bridged by a lock, which however, was not appreciated by the people of Haarlem, who destroyed it and blocked the new connection with a dam. Those of Amsterdam then constructed the *'Overtoom'* that enabled the canal to be used for small barges. The canal is later called *'Overtoomse vaart'* (*vaart* = canal) and the spot appears to have been a popular place for a Sunday outing. There was a tavern or perhaps several that still survive in an old Dutch nursery rhyme. The area has been called *'Overtoom'* until it became part of the municipality of Amsterdam. In 1921 the *'Overtoomse vaart'* was filled in, and is now a street simply called *'Overtoom'*.

In 1685 Cornelius Meijer included in his *L'Arte de restiuire a Roma la tralasciata navigatione* an illustration of a water-power operated inclined plane, overcoming a small change in level at a weir.[10] More primitive devices were found in the United States at a much later date.[11] In 1840 it was reported that on the Susquehannah River in Pennsylvania, at places where there were weirs across the river, there were also inclines made of timber for flat bottomed arks and floats of timber to go down, but not ascend. No doubt such arrangements were found elsewhere in the United States, and today, on the upper Thames, in England, rollers are provided to enable canoes or punts to by-pass locks.

The drawback of these medieval inclines was that the boats were drawn up them without any form of carriage being used to support them. This refinement is first noted in an incline put in at some unknown date, certainly before 1602, at Lizzafusina or Zafosina on the River Brenta, intended to prevent the fresh water of the Brenta from flowing into the salt water of the Venetian lagoon and silting up the lagoon. Boats were transported over the incline by means of two strong cradles on wheels, drawn up by a rope passing over an axle which was worked by a horse-gin. The illustrations of this incline show a double incline but there does not appear to have been any counterbalancing. The wheels of the cradles run in grooves, not on rails.[12]

Leon Battista (1404-72) a Florentine engineer, author of *De re aedificatoria* which was published posthumously in 1485, mentioned the use of windlasses to haul boats up inclines, and goes on to mention primitive locks.[13] The date of the Lizzafusina incline not being exactly known, it may well be as early as the fifteenth century, as pound locks appear to have been used in North Italy by 1500.

Other encyclopædic works illustrating types of machinery in the sixteenth and seventeenth centuries include drawings of broadly similar inclines,[14] but whether such drawings were made from observation or merely as designs of possible machines is never quite clear.

CHAPTER II

MID-EIGHTEENTH-CENTURY INCLINES

During the second half of the eighteenth century, engineers began to plan the extension of canals into terrain where the use of ordinary pound locks was likely to prove difficult owing to sharp contours, or to lack of water. The use of boats smaller than normal canal boats was contemplated, as techniques and materials of the period were not capable of dealing with full size canal boats on inclines or lifts.

In the case of canals built through country lacking a suitable water supply, the smaller profile of the canal made possible by the use of small boats (usually referred to as tub-boats) economised in water.

The first engineer to attempt to use inclines in such circumstances was an Irishman, Davis Ducart, whose real name was Daviso de Arcort. His name has also been found spelt Duchart, Dukart, Ducarte, Ducate, Duckart and even Dularte. He is described as having been formerly an engineer in the Sardinian service, and his name seems to indicate a Franco-Italian origin. Unfortunately all efforts have so far failed to trace him in the archives of the house of Savoy, which had acquired the Kingdom of Sardinia in 1718.

The first record of Ducart in Ireland is in connection with the design of the Customs House at Limerick, started in 1765.[1] Thereafter, until his death, Ducart was employed to design a number of country houses and public buildings — there can be no doubt that he was a talented architect. How he came to turn his attention to the Tyrone Canal is not known, but if he had been in the Sardinian service he might well have been able to observe inland navigation works in Italy.

In 1732 a plan had been made to cut a canal from Coalisland, three or four miles from the collieries at Drumglass in County Tyrone, to the river Blackwater so that coal might travel by water to Lough Neagh, and thence to Newry and Dublin. This would lessen the dependence of Dublin on English coal, supplies of which were apt to be uncertain in winter.[2]

By 1767 the Irish Parliament had decided to extend the navigation from Coalisland to the actual collieries, and a plan of Ducart's was adopted involving the cutting of a tub-boat canal just over four miles long, on which twelve one-ton boats were to be used. The original idea was to cut the canal partly in the open and partly in tunnel to Derry colliery, where a shaft 148 feet deep was to be used for lowering boxes of coal. From the top of the shaft a further length of canal was to run to Drumglass colliery on the level. But in November 1767, when part of the cutting of the canal sections had been done, the plan for a hoist was changed, and Ducart embarked on the construction of three inclines, known locally at the time as 'hurries' or 'dry wherries'. The first was a distance of 942 yards from Coalisland basin with a rise of fifty-five feet, and the second was 844 yards further on at Drumreagh House, with a rise of sixty-five feet.[3]. The third, just west of Farlough Lake, had a rise of seventy feet. In 1773 it seems that official doubts were raised and work was stopped while William Jessop, assistant to John Smeaton, inspected the works. By that time the canal was virtually completed apart from the hurries, which were only partially finished. The report of the inspection was written by Smeaton himself, who had not personally been to Coalisland.[4] It appears that Ducart's first idea was to have timber ramps fitted with rollers, and presumably to haul the boats up by means of water-wheels. The power had proved to be insufficient and Smeaton, while disapproving of the whole scheme as extravagant, suggested that to make the best of a bad job, and avoid throwing away the money already spent, the hurries should be made double, and counterbalancing introduced so that loaded boats going down would haul up empty boats − fortunately traffic would be downhill from the collieries. He also recommended that the size of the boats should be increased from one ton to two tons, and that 'a tackle, assisted by a winch or windlass' should be provided to haul the boats over the sill at the top of the inclines.[5]

William Chapman states that the boats were flat bottomed and flat sided, four feet six inches in width, two feet six inches in height and ten feet in length along the flat side. Boats had one end square and the other pointed, and they worked chained end to end in gangs. A horse-gin was provided to help the boats over the sills. The rollers at first were retained, but as they did not work evenly, Ducart installed rails, to carry a four wheeled cradle on which the boat rested.[6] In a map of 1778[7] the canal is shown as completed, (according to Chapman it was finished in 1777); but as the main navigation between Coalisland and the River Blackwater had not been completed nothing could be done except pass a few boats by way of trial, and by 1787, when the main navigation was finished, the hurries had proved to be unsatisfactory, and Ducart was dead. Arthur Young, in an Appendix to his *Tour in Ireland*[8] remarked that 'Mr. Dularte has not the support which he thinks necessary to do anything effectual.' It sounds as if Young had actually spoken to Ducart; but the failure of the works, which had been most expensive, provide an unspoken criticism of Ducart's work.

In 1787 Richard Owen, the engineer of the extension of the Lagan Navigation from Lisburn to Lough Neagh, was sent by the Corporation for Inland Navigation to inspect the works above Coalisland, and he suggested dismantling the hurries, and substituting gravelled or paved inclined roads. No further traffic passed the hurries, though as they were very solidly built much of the masonry can still be seen.

Thus ended the unhappy history of the extension of the Coalisland Canal.

Even after the sensible suggestions of Jessop or Smeaton had been adopted the hurries were unsatisfactory, possibly due to their slope being too steep to allow safe working by counterbalancing. But shortage of water on the upper levels would almost certainly have rendered any work on the hurries ineffectual.

The object unsuccessfully pursued by Ducart was soon afterwards attained by the self-acting incline put in at the Ketley Ironworks in Shropshire by William Reynolds, a Quaker engineer and partner in the Coalbrookdale works. Born at Ketley on 14 April 1758, his mother being a member of the Darby family, he was trained by his father Richard Reynolds.[9]

In January 1788 William Reynolds wrote to his brother-in-law that he was making a canal from Oakengates to Ketley.[10] This was primarily to transport iron ore and coal from the pits at Oakengates to the Ketley furnaces, and as the loaded traffic was virtually all downhill to the furnaces there was no obstacle to overcoming the steep drop near Ketley furnaces by an incline; locks were out of the question because of the acute lack of water in the area. Reynolds was probably acquainted with both John Smeaton and William Jessop; but whether Reynolds had heard of Ducart's experiments from them is not known. He laid a strong double track railway on a blue brick base, down a slope on the south side of Ketley Hall. At the top of the plane was a double lock, the floor of which had a gentler slope than the incline. Over the lock was a large wooden drum, on which ran a long rope which hauled the boats up and down the incline and was controlled by a brakeman. The boats were carried in wooden cradles having large wheels in front and small wheels at the rear, to keep the boats on an even keel on the incline.[11]

The system of working[12], assuming that an empty boat was coming up the incline, was as follows:

When the cradle with an empty boat entered the lock at the top of the incline, the lock gate would be closed and the lock flooded, becoming virtually part of the upper canal. The empty boat would be manoeuvred off the cradle and another moved on. In the lower basin operations were less complicated, the loaded boat being taken off the cradle and replaced by an empty one. Then the water in the lock at the top of the plane would be drawn off into a side pond, the lock gate would be opened, and with the brakeman in control the cradles would once again be set in motion.[13]

It is an indication of the shortage of water on the canal that it was worth while having a small 'fire-engine' at the top of the incline, not to assist with winding, but to pump water out of the side pond back into the top level.

The boats which operated on the canal were square-ended tub-boats, twenty feet long, six feet four inches wide and three feet ten inches deep, each carrying eight tons.[14] There is not sufficient information to determine the dimensions of the incline. Phillips gave a vertical height of sixty-seven feet including one foot in the lock, but Telford, who was a practical engineer who worked with Reynolds on other jobs and was on the spot at the time, gave seventy-three feet as the vertical height.[15] The late Mr. E.A. Forward considered the gradient quoted by Chapman, which worked out at one in two-and-a-half, as being rather unlikely.[16]

The Ketley incline was obviously a success, and appears on a 'token' issued in 1792 at a time of shortage of copper currency: on this the brakeman can be seen at work. The token was payable at Coalbrookdale and Ketley. On 16 May 1789 Reynolds had written to James Watt: 'our inclined plane answers my most sanguine expectations. We have already let down more than forty boats a day each carrying eight tons — on an average thirty boats a day and have not yet had an accident.'[17]

There is among the drawings in the sketchbook which once belonged to William Reynolds, now in the Science Museum Library, a view of the winding gear used on the Ketley plane, in which the locks and winding drum can be plainly seen.[18] Unfortunately William Reynolds died in 1803, and his brother Joseph who took over the direction of the Ketley works was primarily a banker. Following the end of the Napoleonic wars trade was very bad, so Joseph Reynolds blew out the furnaces and shut the works. The incline never worked again as far as is known. The French engineer Dutens found it disused in 1818. The site of the incline is now hardly possible to make out, the lower basin which provided a reference point having been filled up in 1965.

Among other enterprises, Earl Gower & Co. cut the Donnington Wood Canal from Donnington Wood near Oakengates to Pave Lane on the Newport–Wolverhampton Road between 1765 and July 1768. The Donnington Wood Canal being a private venture and not cut with Parliamentary powers — it lay entirely on Earl Gower's own estate — is a somewhat obscure concern, and this obscurity is not dispelled by its having changed its title with the successive steps in the peerage of its chief owner. It is often referred to as the Marquess of Stafford's Tub-Boat Canal after 1786, and as the Duke of Sutherland's Tub-boat Canal after 1833.

The canal appears to have connected with other navigable levels running into the coal mines in the Donnington Wood area. A plan of the Donnington Wood Colliery dated 1 August 1788 found in the archives of the Lilleshall Company seems to indicate that these levels were connected underground by an inclined plane, no doubt self-acting, and if this is so the fact that John Gilbert (the Duke of Bridgewater's land-agent), was a partner in the enterprise provides a link with the incline next dealt with. There is no further information at present about this Donnington Wood incline and indeed it cannot be said with certainty that it existed.[19]

In conjunction with his canal the Duke of Bridgewater had developed coal mines at Worsley in Lancashire, and a drainage canal had been cut into the hill at Worsley Delph as a continuation of the main Bridgewater Canal, enabling coal to be boated direct to the Manchester area.[20] As the workings went deeper into the hill, it became necessary to make a higher level canal at Walkden thirty-five and a half yards vertically above the original level, and about 1795 John Gilbert prepared a scheme for an inclined plane at Ashton's

Field to connect the two levels and replace vertical shafts. The levels were ten feet four inches wide and eight feet six inches high, the depth of water being three feet seven inches. There was a bed of white rock dipping one in four in the right place which was hollowed out into a tunnel. The plane was 151 yards long, with two locks at the top end which were eighteen yards long. From the top locks a double wagonway descended for ninety-four yards, divided by a brick wall with safety openings, and then joining to form a single wagonway fifty-seven yards long to the lower level. The bottom end of the plane was six feet nine inches underwater so that the loaded boats could float off the plane.[21]

The locks were four feet six inches deep at the north end and eight feet deep at the other end in a cavern made twenty-one feet high to admit a winding drum with a circumference of fifteen feet five inches The main rope was two-and-a-half inches in diameter lapped round with a small cord to prevent wear. At intervals there were eight inch rollers to carry the rope. The boats were taken up and down on carriages thirty feet one inch long by seven feet four inches wide and it was found that a load of four tons coming down could draw up one ton. A barge having been run into the lock, the water was run out of the lock, the barge secured to the carriage which was then attached to the main rope by a carrier rope, and another boat having been attached at the bottom end the plane was set in motion by two man-powered winches which set the main shaft moving. The ascent and descent of the plane was controlled by a brakeman, and the winches were only necessary if a part load was coming up. Thirty loaded boats could be let down in eight hours. The largest boats were fifty feet long and four feet six inches wide and carried twelve tons. As the tare weight was four tons and the carriage weighed about five tons, a total weight of twenty-one tons was moved. Boats carrying seven tons and eight and a half tons were also in use. This incline was put in hand in September 1795, finished in October 1797 and continued to work until 1822.[22] Visits were paid to it by parties of engineers in the 1960s but as the last colliery drained by the canal system has now been closed, in 1969 barriers were built inside the tunnel mouth to raise the water level up to the roof in places to seal in any colliery gases.[23] John Gilbert died in 1795, but the Hon. & Reverend F.H. Egerton (who appears to have had a fair share of the family eccentricity) was emphatic when writing in 1818 that the Duke himself was the 'planner and contriver' of the incline.[24] The work was done under the direction of Benjamin Sothern, at the time the Duke's manager of works and later an official of the Bridgewater Canal.[25]

Such self-acting inclines can only work where traffic is almost entirely downwards. This being somewhat unusual, no self-acting incline has been attempted since the Walkden incline, and it seems highly improbable that conditions favourable to such an arrangement will present themselves in future.

CHAPTER III

POWERED TUB-BOAT CANAL INCLINES

The next group to be considered employed water power – firstly water-wheels and later turbines – to assist tub-boats to surmount inclines, in nearly all cases arranged so that the weight of a descending boat could help to raise an ascending one. This used valuable water, but was not so prodigal in its use as a system of pound locks would have been. These inclines again were on canals built where conditions were normally unfavourable to canal construction. A number were associated with efforts, starting in 1774, to link the Bristol Channel at Bude with the English Channel at Plymouth by canal.[1] An incidental object was to improve the farms of the area by bringing sea sand inland, where it was found to be of great value for dressing the fields. From the first, changes of level were to be effected by inclined planes. The earliest scheme was put forward in conjunction with the first Bude Canal Act, which received the Royal Assent on 24 May 1774.[2] This was projected by John Edyvean (of whom more later) and envisaged a tub-boat canal to accommodate ten-ton boats, with five inclines requiring trans-shipment at each.[3] In 1777 a report was obtained from John Smeaton, who suggested a less ambitious scheme, including two inclines up to the summit level from the Bude River, and one incline down into the Tamar Valley; the exact nature of the proposed inclines is not known, but in the event nothing was done and the Parliamentary powers expired after ten years.

Edmund Leach, who had been one of the Surveyors for the original scheme of 1774, published a *Treatise of Universal Inland Navigations* in 1785,[4] in which he proposed a canal from Bude and Widemouth to Calstock using four inclined planes, on which the tub-boats were to be carried by counterbalanced caissons running on rollers. The motive power was to be provided by waterwheels, although the caissons were to have cisterns of water to help with counterbalancing. The ballast water was to be gradually discharged during the ascent of the plane to ensure a correct balance with the descending caisson. Leach's plans made a considerable impact on opinion, but were never tried out in practice.[5]

In 1793 the Bude Canal project was revived, with the backing of the influential and inventive peer, Charles, 3rd Earl Stanhope, Lord of the Manor of Holsworthy. At a meeting at Holsworthy on 25 October 1793, a scheme was put forward involving the use of small two-ton boats which were to be carried up rails on inclines, suspended between pairs of wheels six feet in diameter *(pendenters)* using horses to drag the boats up and down the inclines. No progress was made with this scheme.

These earlier schemes were taken up by Robert Fulton (1765-1815) the American artist and inventor.[6] He turned to canal designing, and on 8 May 1794 patented 'Machinery for the Conveyance of Canal Boats from one Level to another.'[7] This patent proposed a system of single or double inclines using wheeled cisterns, which were to be filled with water for the descent and would carry boats which were to be hauled onto the cisterns by water power. These could be modified into perpendicular lifts. The boats, as in all the Bude Canal schemes, were to be tub-boats. With encouragement from Lord Stanhope, Fulton produced a *Treatise on the Improvement of Canal Navigation* in 1796. This work suggested the use of tub-boat canals, with inclines worked by the power produced by a bucket filled with water descending a well at the head of the incline, or on shorter inclines the use of waterwheels to provide power. His most striking contribution, first mentioned in his Patent, but developed in the *Treatise*, was that of fitting wheels to the tub-boats, enabling the use of separate carriages on the inclines to be dispensed with.[8] Fulton himself accomplished nothing practical in canal engineering, though he did make a survey for an abortive scheme for a canal with seven inclines from Hayle to Helston in West Cornwall.[9]

His book attracted considerable attention, and was translated into French by a military engineer who was director of the Sambre-Oise Junction Canal, François de Recicourt (1744-1814).[10] This explains why the first practical application of Fulton's ideas was in France, where E.M. Gauthey applied some of the principles to the Canal du Creusot[11], authorised by a law of the year IX (1801) 9 Germinal to extend the rigole de Torcy to the works at Le Creusot. M. Gauthey was a very capable engineer who held the post of Inspector-General of Bridges and Roads at the time of the French Revolution.

The scheme for the Canal du Creusot included a little of everything: commencing from the Torcy intake there were three locks, followed by a stretch with three inclined planes, and the canal was to be completed to the Creusot basin by a section with three vertical lifts (which will be dealt with later). The inclined planes were to be built somewhat after the pattern suggested in Fulton's book, except that the boats were to be carried on 'chariots' attached by a line to an endless rope, which was set in motion by a water-wheel. The canal was 2.6 metres wide and one metre deep, and the boats carried eight tonnes. The three inclined planes were to have falls of 8.61 metres, 5.63 metres and 7.31 metres. By the year XIV (1806) the vertical lift at the Creusot basin, and one of the inclined planes, were ready and were tested. The inclined plane worked satisfactorily, but used too much water, and the need to economise water had been the whole reason for the scheme.[12]

This canal suffered a remarkably similar fate to Ducart's: Gauthey died in 1807 and, deprived of his impetus, the scheme collapsed. In 1809 one of the two engineers responsible for the vertical lifts, M. de Solages, put forward a proposal for inclined planes which were to carry the boats in wet caissons. Whether he was also the designer of the inclined planes of the Canal de Creusot is not made clear.

Fulton's suggestion of wheeled boats had not gone unnoticed, and in 1817, two years after his death, projectors of the Bude Canal called in James Green, Bridge Surveyor for the County of Devon, to produce a survey and report on the possibility of a Canal from Bude to the interior. James Green (1781–1849)[13] was a Birmingham man who, after a period as one of Rennie's assistants, was appointed County Surveyor for Devon in 1808, and held the post till he resigned in 1841. This post allowed him to take outside work, and he became the chief English protagonist of canal inclines and planes. His own designs preferred water to steam as motive power, but then coal was not as cheap or plentiful in Devon and West Somerset as it was in the Coalbrookdale area.

His report, presented to the projectors of the Bude Canal on 14 April 1818[14], canvassed two alternatives – canal or railway. The latter was rejected[15] in favour of a canal on a small scale, nineteen feet wide at the top, ten feet wide at the bottom and three feet deep. He suggested five-ton tub-boats (four of which could be drawn by one horse) fitted with wheels so that they could be drawn up and down water powered inclines. The scheme was adopted, the Bude Harbour & Canal Company obtained its Act,[16] and work began on 23 July 1819.[17]

As built, the works on the Bude Canal included five inclines worked by waterwheel and one – the longest – intended to be worked by Fulton's 'bucket in the well' method. From the Bude end of the canal, the first incline was at Marhamchurch rising 120 feet in a distance of 836 feet. The next was at Hobbacott Down (sometimes referred to as the Thurlibeer or Thurlowbeer incline) rising 225 feet.

Near the Red Post between Hobbacott and Vealand the canal divided, and the longer arm (nominally the branch) proceeded south towards Launceston. On this arm were three inclines: at Merrifield, falling sixty feet and 360 feet long: at Tamerton, falling fifty-nine feet and also 360 feet long, and at Bridgetown or Werrington, falling fifty-one feet and 259 feet long. On the other arm there was an incline at Vealand rising 58 feet and 500 feet long.

The *pièce de résistance* of the Bude Canal inclines was undoubtedly the Hobbacott plane. It was intended to raise and lower the boats with the aid of two enormous buckets each in a well as deep as the difference between the two canal levels. Each bucket was ten feet in diameter and five feet six inches deep, and would hold fifteen tons of water; it was suspended on a chain which passed over a drum, and operated an endless chain running down the incline, to which the boats were attached. This machine proved capable of doing the work for which it was designed provided it was in working order, but unfortunately the chains obtainable in the 1820s did not prove strong enough and there was perpetual trouble with breakages of both the bucket chains and the main drawing chains. A small steam engine was provided at Hobbacott as a standby in the case of breakdowns; whether this was intended from the start, or found to be necessary in practice, is not quite clear. In 1835 there was serious discussion as to whether the bucket system should be suppressed, and a larger steam winding engine installed; but the buckets survived to the end of the canal.

The other inclines on the Bude Canal were worked by waterwheels situated in a pit at the top of the slope, about twenty-eight feet long internally by nine feet six inches in breadth in the case of Merrifield. The pit at Marhamchurch, which had a fifty foot wheel, must have been larger. Each waterwheel worked a drum over which an endless chain running up and down the incline was wound. Again, the machinery proved rather too frail for its duties, and a constant source of anxiety for the overworked and underpaid staff of the canal company. At the same time, when all was in order the system worked well. Marhamchurch incline could raise a boat in five minutes, the buckets at Hobbacott in four minutes. But the whole system suffered from faults. In 1826 for example, the tram rails at Marhamchurch, Hobbacott and Vealand were reported broken. The shafts of the various chain wheels were apt to break, and it is plain that costs of maintenance were very heavy.

The tub-boats were twenty feet by five feet six inches and could carry five tons; they normally navigated in gangs of four or six, the front boat having a pointed bow. The wheels were fourteen inches diameter. As a safety device to guard against runaways on inclines, each boat had an iron bar fitted at the back, intended to dig into the ground and stop the boat running backwards.

The Bude Canal survived for many years, but gradually the approach of the railway system sapped its traffic. In 1877 the boiler and engine at Hobbacott were worn out and were scrapped, the incline depending thereafter on the buckets.[18] The Company struggled on till November 1891, when notice of closure of the tub-boat section of the line was given. This was the last survivor of the tub-boat canals and certainly the system of wheeled boats and inclines had proved workable.

James Green remained Engineer to the Bude Canal Company till 1832, although it is uncertain whether he took much part in the actual construction. He was also responsible for another canal nearby, which has received little attention since it was a private venture of Lord Rolle (1750-1842), who is best known for having tripped over his robes at Queen Victoria's coronation and *rolled* down the aisle. This was the Rolle or Torrington Canal, cut without parliamentary authority between 1824 and 1827.[19] At Ridd, near Weare Giffard, a mile above the sea-lock, there was a double tracked incline up to the summit level.

Fortunately a photograph of the arrangements at the head of the incline has survived. From a study of this photograph, and the pit at the head of the

13

incline, Barry Hughes[20] concludes that like the shorter Bude inclines, it was worked by a waterwheel in the pit, driving an endless chain running over large horizontal overhead wheels at the top and bottom of the incline, to which the boats were attached by a short length of chain. Boats had to be helped over the sill at the top by some form of bar at the side of the sill. It appears from the photograph that the waterwheel drove a vertical shaft, which engaged in internal cogs on the circumference of the overhead wheel at the top. The boats appear to have been similar to those on the Bude Canal, fitted with wheels, and were normally navigated in trains of six, although of course they could only be hauled up or down the incline singly. A descending boat would to some extent counterbalance a rising boat, but loaded traffic was mostly up the incline in practice, so that counterbalancing would not be very effective.

In 1950 the author spoke to a man then aged seventy-three at Limekiln Cottages, Annery, who said his mother had been born in the cottages and had died there aged eighty-three. He had been told that the incline was worked by a waterwheel, and that the boats had wheels.

This incline continued to work till the canal was superseded by the Bideford & Torrington Railway which was opened on 18 July 1872:[21] presumably the incline closed during 1871 to allow the railway to be built across the top of it. The chief traffic on the Rolle Canal was limestone for fertiliser and coal.

James Green's next venture was as Engineer of the Grand Western Canal, which had been originally formed in 1796 to build a canal from Taunton to Topsham, with a branch to Tiverton.[22] This was intended to open a communication between the Bristol Channel and the English Channel for barges fourteen feet six inches wide carrying up to fifty tons. By 1814 the eleven mile section between Tiverton and Lowdwells on the Devon-Somerset border had been built at enormous expense. This was a single level, but the section required to connect Lowdwells to Taunton down the Tone Valley remained to be cut. This presented a difference in levels of 262 feet and was through exceedingly broken country at the western end. As it was plain that the cost and difficulties of water supply of a full size canal would be prohibitive, the Company considered a plan put forward by James Green at a public meeting at Exeter on 1 May 1829. Pointing out that the maximum width of the navigations east of Taunton was less than the capacity of the existing Grand Western Canal, Green proposed a canal for tub-boats which could be hauled in trains of up to eight by a single horse. In his first report Green suggested changes of levels by three inclines, but later he put forward a scheme for the use of one incline and seven lifts. On 13 April 1830 a general meeting of the canal proprietors, held in London, approved the scheme incorporating the lifts and work was put in hand on 13 June 1831. Unfortunately the Grand Western Canal proved to be Green's Waterloo, and while the lifts, as will be seen, were successful once teething troubles were overcome, Wellisford incline was only too obviously defective. Possibly misled by the comparative success of the Hobbacott incline,

Green produced a design which proved hopelessly inadequate. As the tub-boats on the Grand Western Canal were twenty-six feet long by six feet six inches wide, and drew two feet three inches when loaded, weighing eight tons, they were too large to be tipped up and run up the incline on their own wheels, and so Wellisford was fitted with two tracks, and cradles to carry the boats up and down. If it had been possible to arrange for loaded boats to be passing up and down simultaneously, the extra power required to move the cradles would not be great: but with a loaded boat going up unbalanced, a good deal of power was needed. Yet for some reason – possibly failure to remember that in practice counterbalancing would be the exception – Green not only chose to work the incline (which was 440 feet long, rising eighty-one feet at a slope of about one in five-and-a-half) by the tub in the well method, without any auxiliary steam, but provided only ten-ton buckets whereas the Hobbacott buckets were fifteen-ton. He may have thought that a shorter incline would not need so much power, and that a boat in a cradle would present less friction than a wheeled boat. As there is a good deal of evidence that he was an obstinate man who did not take kindly to advice, probably no-one dared point out the deficiency in design till it was too late. On 27 January 1836 the Committee of the Canal dismissed Green and called in a consultant, W.A. Provis, who had been assistant to Telford on the Holyhead Road, and had a great deal of canal experience, notably as a contractor on the Birmingham and Liverpool Junction Canal. He inspected the inclines at Hobbacott and Wellisford, and found the latter unsatisfactory.[23] A twelve-horse-power steam engine was bought for installation at Wellisford and proved able to raise a boat and load weighing seven tons in five minutes, under test.[24] Only a few years later the Grand Western Canal met overwhelming rail competition, and in 1867 the tub-boat section was closed and the incline and lifts dismantled.

In 1833, or possibly late in 1832,[25] James Green was again employed by canal projectors, this time to prepare a scheme for a canal from the Bridgwater & Taunton Canal at Creech St. Michael to Chard. This involved crossing three ranges of hills, and Green's plan called for two lifts and two inclined planes.[26] In June 1834 the Chard Canal Company obtained its Act, but presumably in view of the troubles which Green was having a few miles away on the other side of Taunton, he was not engaged as engineer, nor were the two lifts included in the scheme. The distinguished and versatile engineer, Sir William Cubitt (1785-1861) was consulted and, according to his son Joseph Cubitt, was responsible for the design of the four inclines, two of which at Thornfalcon and Wrantage only rose twenty-eight feet and twenty-seven feet six inches respectively.[27] According to James Leslie,[28] at Wrantage the boats (which were twenty-five feet or twenty-six feet in length and six feet six inches wide, like Grand Western tub-boats) were carried afloat in a caisson with six wheels twenty-eight feet six inches long and six feet nine inches wide, with doors opening inwards. It was a double incline, operated by a chain running round a horizontal drum or sheave at the top. Motion was communicated by running more water into the descending than into the ascending caisson. Brakes were fitted to control the motion. The gradient was one in eight. Leslie did not mention the Thornfalcon incline, but said that the Ilminster incline was similar to Wrantage. This was a mistake for Thornfalcon was described in a contemporary article in similar terms to Wrantage.[29] A drawing has recently come to light which shows that the Ilminster incline, rising eighty two and a half feet at one in nine, was worked by an overshot waterwheel at the foot of the incline operating what appears to be an endless chain through gearing.[30] The fourth incline, at Chard Common, had a single line of rails, and a turbine at the foot of the incline took boats on a four wheeled carriage dry over the summit and into the top level. This incline rose eighty-six feet by a gradient of one in eight. The turbine was by Whitelaw & Stirrat, working on a head of twenty-five feet and a flow of 725 cubic feet per minute.[31]

Thornfalcon and Wrantage inclines appear to have been ready and working by 27 July 1841: the Ilminster incline was tried out on 3 February 1842: and the Chard incline on 24 May 1842. The engineer to the Canal Company was Sydney Hall, who was only twenty-two when appointed. Whether Hall merely carried out designs by Sir William Cubitt is not known, but certainly the inclines on the Chard Canal are not similar to any of Green's known designs. The canal went into receivership in 1853 and probably closed in February 1868, the machinery on the inclines being sold in 1869. The inclines seem to have suffered from the usual rope or chain breakages.[32]

In 1833 James Green was called in by the proprietors of the Kidwelly & Llanelly Canal and Tramroad Company to report on the improvement and extension of their undertaking, and he recommended the extension of the Gwendraeth Valley line of canal from Pontyates to Cwm-mawr Bridge, with three inclined planes. This proposal was adopted, and in 1834 work started. The proposal was to have inclined planes at Pont Henry, with a vertical rise of fifty-seven feet at a gradient of one in six, at Capel Ifan with a vertical rise of fifty-six feet at a gradient of one in six, and a third incline, apparently never completed, at Hirwaun-isaf, intended to have a vertical rise of eighty-three feet at one in ten.[33] The best information available about the power is: 'The inclines were manipulated by hydraulic pumps which were considered to be great discoveries.'[34] It has also been stated that 'coal was conveyed over them in trams, and at one time barges were brought down the inclines on long trollies. They were brought up the inclines by a balance weight running on rails.'[35] An article written in 1867 of uncertain authority refers to 'the arrangements for letting down the boats by a self-acting incline.'[36]

It seems clear that only the lower inclines were completed. The Pont Henry incline is shown on the railway deposited plan of 1865 as being double tracked, and probably the Capel Ifan incline was similar.[37] As far as is known the canal was not used for traffic above Pontyberem, a narrow gauge tramway being laid by a local coalowner along the towpath and up the incline to Cwm-mawr. The boats on the Gwendraeth Valley inclines carried about six tons each and worked in gangs of four.[38] It would be tempting to think that they were wheeled but there is no evidence of this. As James Green ceased to be Engineer on 30 January 1836, only three days after he had been dismissed by the Grand Western Canal Company, work on the top incline may have been suspended then. The inclines closed when the Burry Port and Gwendraeth Valley Railway was built from Burry Port to Pontyberem, opening in July 1869. The chief traffic was coal, downwards.

This was as far as is known the last of James Green's tub-boat inclines and we now turn to the tub-boat canals in Shropshire, where coal was readily available, and steam power used for a system of inclines which proved highly successful in its time.

In January 1788, William Reynolds was engaged in cutting the Shropshire Canal from Oakengates to Coalport. This presented problems of levels not soluble by self-acting inclines of the Ketley type, the traffic not being predominently downhill. As designed, the canal was to rise to a summit level near Donnington Wood and fall from a place near Stirchley to the Severn at Coalport by inclined planes at the Windmill, Stirchley and at the Hay, Coalport. The canal committee were uncertain as to how to deal with these changes in level; the shortage of water on the summit level made locking quite out of the question, apart from the waste of time involved in passing as many locks as would be necessary. On the 16 May 1789, William Reynolds wrote from Ketley to James Watt, enquiring whether Watt had any ideas on the subject, as the canal was then navigable almost to Donnington Wood.[39]

Reynolds mentions that the inclined plane at Ketley 'answers my most sanguine expectations' so that it is plain that the difficulty was that the duties expected of the plane were different from those met at Ketley.

On 18 July 1788 the Clerk of the Shropshire Canal Company had written to James Watt asking the same question; and on 13 July 1788 he had advertised in London, Birmingham and Shrewsbury papers offering a premium of fifty guineas for a suitable plan for 'the best means of lowering and raising heavy weights from one navigation to another'. The various schemes put forward in reply to this advertisement were examined by a committee of the Canal Company, who called in James Watt and John Wilkinson, the ironmaster, as 'persons of science' to assist them. A prize of fifty pounds each was given to John Lowden (who was then the canal surveyor) of Snedshill, Salop, and Henry Williams of Ketley.

What exactly they proposed is not known, and the models they made to illustrate the scheme which were 'to be seen either at Ketley or Snedshill' have long since disappeared. As Reynolds was still ventilating the question in May 1789, it sounds as if the committee were not entirely happy with the winning scheme.

As constructed, the machinery at the three inclined planes did not include a lock at the top as at Ketley, but a sill with a counterslope to run cradles carrying the boats into the top level without any loss of water. The cradles had wheels of different sizes, but the danger of tipping the boat at an angle into the top level was surmounted by fixing an additional pair of wheels to the outside beam of the cradle. These ran on rails along the dockside of the top basin, dipping slightly towards the water level. On these wheels coming into contact with their rails they lifted the smaller cradle wheels off their rails and allowed the cradle and boat to enter the water of the top basin at an acceptable angle. One boat was then floated off and another floated onto the cradle and secured by chains. The inclines were double tracked, and over the sill at the top were large drums on which the ropes — later chains — which drew the boats up and down were coiled. There were also secondary drums on which ropes were coiled for pulling the boats over the sills. The problem of getting the boats over the sills at the top, and down the counterslopes was originally solved by the use of some apparatus, probably a horse gin or capstan, but on 17 January 1791 a steam engine was ordered for Donnington Wood incline, on 27 October 1792 one for the Windmill incline and on 19 December 1792 one for the Hay incline. As the traffic would predominently be downwards on the two latter inclines, the late Mr. E.A.Forward felt[40] that in all probability it was hoped to work by counterbalancing (with a certain amount of help from a horse gin at the top), but in practice the Donnington Wood incline was worked almost entirely by the engine, while the engines at the Windmill and the Hay were used to start a movement, and then normally idled, allowing the falling boat to pull up the rising boat; the engine being brought in again at the end to control the movement, and help the rising boat over the sill and into the top level. That the planes were worked before steam power was actually available is plain from the canal committee in 1796 instructing the superintendent, in case of a refusal to pay tolls on the part of canal users, to 'put up machinery of the same kind that was originally placed at the incline . . . and . . . take down the engine and ropes'.

The Donnington Wood incline was 350 yards long, rising 120 feet vertically: the Windmill incline was 600 yards long with a vertical fall of 126 feet and the Hay fell 207 feet.[41] E.A. Forward concluded that the length of the Hay was 300 yards, but von Oeynhausen & von Dechen give it as 793 feet, and in view of the painstaking nature of their enquiries this is not to be overlooked.

Most of the information which we have relates to the Hay incline, which seems to have been shown to visiting engineers as a showpiece. The German engineers described the rails as the strongest and thickest that they had seen. They lay on fourteen inch square timbers, and these upon wooden cross sleepers. The rails were seventy-two inches long, eight inches wide (including the flange) and two inches thick.[42]

When Dutens saw the Hay incline in 1818, and when the incline was photographed about 1879, there were two independent tracks, but when the Germans visited the place in 1826-7 the centre rails had been combined, except where the cradles crossed each other in the middle of the incline.

Dutens gives the gauge as fifty-two and three-quarter inches, and the Germans as forty-three inches – no doubt they measured the gauge in different ways.

Another curious point[43] is that when one of Watt's assistants, John Southern, visited two of the inclines on 29 May 1795, he reported that they had engines of the type designed by Heslop, and William Reynolds Anstice of the Madeley Wood Company said that he remembered Heslop engines at the Hay and Windmill inclines. Southern criticized these engines adversely, and in September 1795 the Canal Company decided to sell the large engine at the Windmill; but this would be before W.R.Anstice's time. Both Dutens and the German engineers describe the engine at the Hay as being single cylinder, whereas Heslop engines had two cylinders. Again, W.R. Anstice said that the Heslop type Hay engine was changed for a Boulton & Watt 'about thirty years ago' (writing in 1879). It is of course possible that Southern did not see the Hay, but Donnington Wood and Windmill, and that the Heslop engine at the Hay was installed after 1826. It is most annoying that the drawings of Donnington Wood inclined plane engine, dated 28 September 1793, in William Reynolds' sketchbook[44] merely show the engine to have been a beam engine. Drawings of the incline gear in both Dutens' and Plymley's books show the engine on the west side of the canal, not the east, and on the ground there is no sign of this having been so. If it is the case that the drawings were both reversed in printing when the blocks were made, (the only likely explanation) it is an odd coincidence.

The boats used on the canal were eighteen feet long and five feet wide, and two-and-a-half feet deep: they held five tons loaded and then had only three inch freeboard. The combined weight of a cradle (two tons) boat (one-and-a-half tons) and cargo (five tons) would normally be eight-and-a-half tons.[42]

According to the German engineers, the system of working at the Hay incline was as follows:[45]

> As soon as the full wagon comes to the bottom, the laden boat is removed by a workman and pushed into the canal, and, in exchange, an empty boat is brought on and affixed. The full down-going boat does not draw up the empty one the whole distance, because the tramroad goes entirely under the surface in the lower canal, and the loaded boat, as soon as it plunges into the water, loses much of its weight. As soon as the empty boat stops, a workman releases the brake on the large rope drum, while another puts the engine in connection with this drum and sets it in motion so that the boat shall continue its journey upwards and across the ridge of the self-acting plane. When the boat has reached the ridge it goes slowly on the tramroad into the upper canal. The large rope-drum is then disconnected from the engine, the engine stopped, and two workmen push the empty boat off the wagon, put on a full one instead, and attach the wagon to the chain of the small drum. This chain was unwound during the time that the

empty boat was passing over the ridge, at which time also the chain-drum was connected with the engine. As soon as the full boat is pushed on, the engine is started, and, by means of the chain, draws the full boat upwards out of the canal on to the ridge of the self-acting plane. One workman stands at the engine, the other at the brake. As soon as the boat is across, it is attached to the rope of the large drum and let down the plane by means of the brake. To permit this, the engine is stopped, and the chain-drum disconnected from it; this done, the workman removes the chain from the wagon, and puts on the brake, keeping it on until the full boat plunges into the water at the lower canal. In between, a workman has time to attend to the firing of the engine, and to bring the boats into position and attach them, so that little time is lost. The workman at the lower canal is also employed in the unloading etc., as affixing and detaching the boats requires little time.

The actual passage of a boat is said to have taken only three-and-a-half minutes, and up to one hundred boats had been passed in a day. In its early years the canal was used for great quantities of traffic, but as the nineteenth century wore on, the machinery grew old, subsidence from coal mining increasingly caused trouble, and extreme measures had to be adopted to keep water in the summit level. Between 1845 and 1857 sporadic negotiations went on to merge the canal into the Shropshire Union Canal system, and eventually it was taken over by the London & North Western Railway Company in 1857. In 1856 Mr. Beech, the resident engineer, reported that . . . 'the Donnington Wood incline itself at the upper end is sinking rapidly and a fissure 3 in. wide has appeared in the engine house and walls supporting the drum. This will certainly cause us great inconvenience and expense and a large outlay will be necessary to keep the incline at work' and in 1858: 'I beg to draw your attention to the state of works at this incline, the drum barrel and winding out shaft are so near to the rails that the carriage head touches on passing under we shall therefore be compelled to raise the whole of the machinery'. Apart from this, breakage of the ropes (later chains) on the inclines caused numerous alarming runaways. As early as 8 May 1801, the Canal company was paying compensation to Mr. W. Botfield for repairs to four boats damaged by a chain breaking on the Hay. When a chain broke, if the brakeman was alert he could stop the unrolling of the main cylinder and prevent both boats from running away. A case is recorded where a runaway boat bounced on the lower basin, cleared two other boats and landed in the Severn, close to a ferry boat, into which it pitched some of its cargo of pig iron;[46] and this was not by any means unique.

Following the railway takeover it appears that the canal between the foot of Donnington Wood and the foot of Windmill incline was closed on 1 June 1858.[47] The Hay incline continued for some years, though engines had to be employed pumping water into the upper level of the canal. It is not clear when the Hay incline was last used, but in 1899 it is described as having been derelict for five years.[48]

There were two other inclines linked to the Shropshire Canal, one on the Donnington Wood Canal and the other on the tub-boat section of the Shrewsbury Canal. At Hugh's Bridge on the Donnington Wood Canal there was a branch running north towards Lilleshall, and to connect the two levels an incline was put in about 1790, falling from the main line of the canal. There was an engine house at the top of the incline. A survey made in 1951 showed that the length of the incline was 363 feet and the slope about one in ten. There was room for two lines of rails on the incline.[49] A Miss White, who spent her childhood at the Incline Cottage at Hugh's Bridge, said the incline ceased to work in 1879 but it may have ceased as early as 1873.[50]

The date of 1879 is supported by the fact that a Mrs. K. Talbott who was born in 1870, could remember the incline working, and was of the opinion that the cradle carrying the boats was similar to the Trench incline cradle when shown a picture of the latter. She could recall the splash made by the cradle as it entered the lower level.

The last man to work the incline was also the last operator of the Windmill Incline, William Mansell. What a pity he did not leave his memoirs![51] The boats were similar to those on the Shropshire Canal, as there was through working. No details are known of the engine.

Finally, there was the famous incline at Trench, on the tub-boat section of the Shrewsbury Canal (later part of the Shropshire Union system), which survived to be the last working incline in the United Kingdom.[52]

The Shrewsbury Canal provided the link between the tub-boat system and the remainder of the canal system of England, though how far the tub-boats worked beyond the foot of the Trench incline is not clear. The incline, authorised by the Shrewsbury Canal Act of June 1793, was 223 yards long, and rose seventy-five feet vertically. At the first meeting of shareholders of the canal it was decided: 'that an engine, similar to the one at Donnington Wood be erected at the head of the intended inclined plane at Wombridge, and that William Reynolds be requested to order the engine from the Coalbrookdale Company and to forward the erection of it with all expedition.' At the end of August 1794, Emanuel Galiere was appointed 'to superintend the fire engine at the inclined plane'. At first a charge was made for tonnage passing over the plane, but on 1 March 1827 the Company dispensed with the charge.

The incline was of similar design to the three on the Shropshire Canal. After the opening of the Newport branch of the Shropshire Union Canal, which provided a connection to the main canal system, traffic increased, and in 1842 a fresh engine was obtained from the Coalbrookdale Company on approval and later accepted. It is described as 'a high pressure engine on the Cornish plan, capable of working from fifteen to twenty-five horsepower'. Frank Owen who worked on the incline latterly as brakeman, from 1890 till the close of traffic, said that this engine, which lasted to the end, would do all that was required of it on ten pound of steam, and 'blew its cock' when twenty pound showed on the gauge. In 1841 the Canal ordered two patent wire ropes 300 yards long and half-an-inch thick, but in September 1842 another was ordered 306 yards long and one inch thick. In 1844 an iron cradle was ordered from the Coalbrookdale Company.

According to Frank Owen ten boats could pass the incline each way in an hour 'when they were running', i.e. when partly loaded boats were being passed up the incline: when empty boats were raised progress was slower as more use had to be made of the brake. On a normally busy day fifty to sixty boats would move over the plane in either direction. The traffic in later days was coal down and wheat up to a mill at Donnington. However, traffic fell off after the First World War due to the exhaustion of the local coal mines and road competition, and the incline closed for traffic on 31 August 1921. The site of the incline is now somewhat overgrown, but traceable.

Early in the nineteenth century at the Millhill branch of the Tavistock Canal in Devon, there was an incline which served a slate quarry which was introduced because of the extreme shortage of water at the summit level, although the height to be surmounted was only nineteen-and-a-half feet, according to von Oeynhausen and von Dechen.[53] This carried tub-boats, thirty feet long, four-and-a-half feet wide and two-and-a-half feet deep, holding about four-and-a-half tons. The cast-iron tramroad was 156 fathoms (936 feet) in length and seventy-and-a-half inches in gauge; it rose only one-and-a-half inches per fathom (six feet). The German engineers say:

A wagon about 20 ft. long moves on this tramroad, and can be let down so deep in the water that the boat can proceed on to it, whereupon boat lading and wagon, together about 8 tons, are brought from one part of the canal to the other by three horses. The empty boat is brought upwards, and the laden one downwards, by one horse. The rails are 8 ft. long, $3\frac{1}{2}$ in. wide without the flange, and 1 in. thick: the flange is 1 in. high, 1 in. thick at the bottom, and $\frac{1}{4}$ in. thick at the top. Each rail has three oblong holes by which it is spiked to thick wooden sleepers laid 3 ft. apart. The 20 ft. long wagon consists of a thick plank framework; the wheels are of cast iron and 24 in. diameter, disc shaped and only $\frac{3}{4}$ in. thick.

The Mill Hill branch was finished before the end of January 1819 and was seen by the German engineers in 1826 or 1827, but it appears to have been closed some time between 1831 and 1844 and was not re-opened, a tramway being substituted.[54] The engineer responsible may have been John Taylor, who was appointed engineer to the canal in 1803, at the age of twenty-three. He was then manager of Wheal Friendship and primarily a mining engineer.

This is the last tub-boat incline to be dealt with, and it seems most improbable that tub-boat canals will ever be built again. They were introduced to meet a requirement, transport in hilly and waterless country, which is now much better met by use of rail or road, and although some of them were most successful within their limitations, the conditions which favoured them have now gone, and seem unlikely to recur. The use of counterbalancing, steam, water power or horses as motive power also seems now to be outmoded.

CHAPTER IV

THE FULL SIZE CANAL INCLINE NINETEENTH AND EARLY TWENTIETH CENTURY

During the nineteenth and early twentieth centuries, a number of engineers designed and built inclines suitable for medium-sized canal boats. The motive power for these ran through horse, water and steam and culminated in electricity. The latter has proved the most successful, though there are still a few inclines in use which employ water power. In the earlier inclines of this period, the boats were carried up and down the incline longitudinally, which led to problems of 'surging' of the water in the caissons where the boats were carried wet. In 1900, however, transverse caissons were employed on the Foxton incline, and the use of these seems to have solved that problem.

To commence with one interesting incline, the whereabouts of which is not certain: William Gravatt mentioned that at an incline under his control, it was found more advantageous to unload barges by barrows and horse runs than to use horse power to draw the barges over the summit.[1] This was evidently a very primitive affair. Gravatt did not give any clue as to where it was, but Gravatt was the engineer for the Parrett Navigation in Somerset, completed in 1841.[2] In that Company's Minute Book for 17 August 1854, in the annual report, it states that a communication had been formed between the river and Langport Station on the Yeovil branch of the B & E R, opened in October 1853. This sounds like an incline intended to carry boats up to a basin where interchange with the railway could take place, and would fit in well with the expressions used by Gravatt, which rather suggest that cargoes were not required to be waterborne far beyond the incline. This incline like the Mill Hill incline on the Tavistock Canal was horse worked, and plainly horse power was not sufficient to work an incline for even medium sized boats.

The earliest water-worked incline suitable for full size boats was put in on the South Hadley Canal on the Connecticut River, U.S.A., in the early 1790s. This was to convey boats and rafts of timber round the South Hadley falls, and was constructed by the Proprietors of the Locks and Canals on the Connecticut River, a company formed in 1792. The engineer responsible was Benjamin Prescott of Northampton, Mass., who later became Superintendent of the Springfield Armory.[3].

A dam was built at the head of the falls, and just above this point the canal started, extending two-and-a-quarter miles down river. At the lower end of the canal an inclined plane at a slope of 13·5° fifty-three feet in height and 230 feet in length, was built of local stone, covered with strong planking. The outlet of the canal was secured by a lock. When boats were to be conveyed down the inclined plane, they passed through the lock and were received through folding doors into a carriage, in which there was enough water to float the boat. When the boat was within the carriage, the lock and the folding doors were closed and the water let out of the carriage through sluices. The carriage was then let slowly down the incline on three sets of wheels, the second and third sets being so much larger than the first as to keep the carriage exactly level.

The machinery by which the carriage was raised or lowered consisted of a waterwheel sixteen feet in diameter on each side of the incline, on the axis of which was wound a strong iron chain, fastened to the carriage. To lower the carriage a gate was opened at the bottom of the canal, and the water passing through turned the wheels; the chain was then unwound allowing the carriage to proceed to the foot of the plane by its own weight. The process was reversed to draw the carriage up.

This installation was not altogether satisfactory; the canal was not deep enough, and cables which were at first used had to be replaced by chains, and even these were frequently broken in service. Furthermore the dam caused the water to back up in the river for ten miles and the inhabitants of Northampton, Mass., found themselves suffering from malaria ('fever and ague').

Consequently, after legal and political pressure had been applied, about 1805 the incline was given up in favour of locks, the dam removed, and the canal deepened so that it filled without the aid of the dam.[4]

The boats used on this canal were from fifty to sixty-five feet long, carrying from ten to twenty-five tons. Upwards of seven thousand tons of merchandise passed through the canal in a season.

During the nineteenth century two further single non-counterbalancing inclines were constructed with some success, the first being at Georgetown on the Chesapeake & Ohio Canal in the U.S.A.[5] For some years in the early 1870s there had been great congestion at Georgetown, the eastern end of the canal, caused by insufficient wharfage for unloading cargoes of coal from the Cumberland coalmines. By locking down into the Potomac River it was possible to reach other wharves, but the only connection was a small lock at the extreme end of the wharves at Georgetown. Construction of an adequate lock would consume water which could not be spared, since shortage of water on the Georgetown level occurred frequently. The former chief engineer of the canal company, William Rich Hutton (1826-1901) who had been retained as consulting engineer, put forward a proposal for an inclined plane using a water-filled caisson moving endwise on the plane. This caisson was 112 feet long, sixteen feet nine inches wide and seven feet ten inches high, resting on six six-wheeled trucks and moving on two pairs of iron rails 600 feet long at a slope of one in twelve. The vertical interval between the canal and the river was forty feet. There were two counterweights, one on each side of the caisson, and steel ropes connected to the end of the caisson ran one left and one right through pulleys at the top of the incline, down to the counterweight, round a sheave on the counterweight and back to an anchorage at the head of the incline. Power was provided by a turbine taking water from the canal and driving onto the pulleys by a system of rods and gearing.

The work was put out to tender, and the successful firm was the Vulcan Ironworks of Baltimore, who supplied caisson, counterweights, machinery and rails. Two 760 feet lengths of one-and-a-quarter inch steel wire rope was supplied by John A. Roebling's sons; Poole & Hunt of Baltimore supplied a twenty-six-and-a-half inch Leffel turbine. Work started on the masonry and civil engineering works in Spring 1875, tenders were invited for the machinery in June 1875, and the incline was completed in the Spring of 1876.

The system of operation was that the caisson was held against the headwall at the top by a hydraulic cylinder. Gates in the canal and the caisson were opened to flood the caisson, and the canal boat admitted; the gates were closed and the caisson lowered until the water level in the river and the caisson were equal, the other gates of the caisson were opened and the boat passed into the river. It would have been possible to adjust the depth of water in the caisson so that by its weight alone the boat and caisson would descend the incline but Hutton considered this would be dangerous in practice, and the system was to arrange the water level so that the weight of boat, water and caisson was approximately equal to the counterweights; the turbine then had merely to overcome the frictional forces. There were two systems of braking, a pawl and ratchet system and 'automatic friction brakes'. To pass a boat took from twelve to eighteen minutes.

The incline was actually owned by the Potomac Lock and Dock Company, and after six months trial, on 11 January 1877, the canal company agreed to lease the incline for twenty-five years at $15,000 per annum, the first boat having passed on 29 June, 1876.

The subsequent history of the incline was uniformly unfortunate. From the commercial point of view its opening coincided with the peak of the canal's prosperity.[6] Congestion of the canal was soon a thing of the past, although traffic was still heavy on the incline in September 1878. In late 1879 constant working of the incline ceased. After August 1880 it became the only link between the canal and the river. During the fall of 1876 while the Company's workmen were balancing the counterweights, the caisson ran away upwards striking the headwall while the counterweights ran down until brought up by the cables — the automatic brakes had been removed because they proved ineffective. In March 1877 there was another incident when the operator noticed that one of the winding pulleys was not running true. The axle turned out to be cracked, presumably owing to the material not being able to withstand the heavy load — the loaded caisson would be about 400 tons, the counterweights twenty tons each. But on 30 May 1877 the masonry supporting one of the winding pulleys gave way; the wire ropes came free, and the loaded caisson and counterweights ran down to the river. The Assistant Harbourmaster, John Mead, was killed and his two assistants were either killed or injured − accounts vary − by the lashing of the wire ropes.

Following this accident Hutton replaced the original iron rails with steel ones, devised an improved method of braking, and adopted heavier winding pulleys. Thereafter, the caisson was operated dry to reduce the load on the machinery. The President of the canal company commissioned a report from P.H. Dudley (1843-1924) a railway engineer who specialised in wheel and axle loads. His report, submitted in May 1879, recommended various changes designed to distribute the load of the caisson more evenly, reduce the possibility of the caisson running out of control, and reduce slipping of the wire ropes. Hutton attempted to refute the report, but he had to admit that the 'excessive pressure of the wheels upon the rails' was the chief defect of the incline. No changes were in fact made, as the canal company was running short of funds, but the incline continued to operate till the Great Flood of 30 May − 1 June 1889 totally wrecked the canal, including the incline. The latter was never rebuilt. Only a bit of the masonry remains.

Although one of the less successful canal inclines, Georgetown attracted a great deal of attention, being selected to represent American Civil Engineering at the Paris International Exposition of 1878. It is known that in that year 1,918 boats used it (an average boat carrying 112 tons of coal), so that even after the accident, which understandably shook the nerve of many of the canal boat captains, the incline saw considerable use. It has recently been said that during the incline's lifetime, 'a steam power arrangement replaced water power, probably because of too much water consumption by the turbine.'[7]

The exhibiting of the model of the Georgetown incline at Paris evidently bore fruit, for M. Jules Fournier, a canal haulier of the town of Meaux near Paris, 'a man of progress and initiative', had long been worried by the fact that the only way of passing a boat from the Canal de l'Ourcq to the River Marne (which passed less than 1 km from the canal at Meaux), was to send it all the way to Paris, through the St. Martin Canal into the Seine, and thence up to the Marne, a round trip of more than 100 km. He formed a private company to construct a connection between the canal and the river, designed to accommodate the canal boats called *Flûtes de l'Ourcq*, twenty-eight metres long, 3.1 metres wide and drawing 1.20 metres. They weighed sixteen tonnes empty and seventy to seventy-five tonnes loaded.[8]

At a place called Beauval, near the Basses-Fermes weir, the two water-courses were only 550 metres apart, the vertical distance between the two being 12.17 metres. As a series of locks would have drained water from the canal, which was unacceptable, an incline was put in following the plans of MM Sautier and Lemonnier, machine builders of Paris. The lower basin, which was thirty-five metres by sixty-six metres, was connected to the

Marne by a cut 373 metres long coming out just above the weir mentioned above (to avoid a further fall). The upper and lower basins were connected by a line of rails rising to a peak and then falling to the lower basin. On these rails ran a carriage on two four-wheeled bogies. A turbine at the lower end of the incline was worked by the water of the Marne (the head of water being the same as the height of the Basses-Fermes weir, about 1.60 metres).

The carriage, made of sheet metal, was twenty-four metres long. Its upper portion was of planking, on which the boats lay, sticking out two metres at each end. The carriage was moved by an arrangement of an endless chain which hauled the carriage along a chain on the bed of the incline, but this was found to produce great vibration and the carriage tended to move in jerks; the chain suffered from breakages, and at first the incline was only used for the passing of boats owned by M. Fournier, and empty boats. This system had been devised by a M. Agudio. According to official sources, the incline was originally built in 1884.

In 1888, M. Fournier consulted M. Nicholas Riggenbach of rack railway fame, and the chain was replaced by a rack placed between the rails, which engaged with a cogwheel on the carriage and was worked by the carriage's transmission system. The new system was supplied by Le Creusot works, and apparently gave complete satisfaction. It was said to be the second rack railway in France. In order to keep the carriage on an even keel, the bogie wheels had flanges on each side, and at the ends of the incline the wheels changed from one set of rails to another. For example, if the carriage was at the lower basin, its front bogie was also on its inner flange on a special rail, so calculated that at a certain point it transferred to the running rail on its outer flange. At the top, the outer wheel flanges of the front carriage ran onto a special rail which lifted the front bogie off the running rail, the back bogie continuing on the running rail.

The carriage moved at a speed of twenty-five metres per second, the total weight of carriage and loaded boat being about 110 tonnes. It appears that only one man was needed to work the incline, as the crews were responsible for manoeuvring the boats on and off the carriage. According to a description written in 1892, more than 1,000 boats had passed since the installation of the rack system without a single accident.

This incline ceased to function in 1922, and in 1950 official sources reported that nothing remained of the installation.[9] The reason for its disuse is not known, but the increase in the size of canal boats may have been responsible.

An incline in South Wales of which little is known is marked on a map of 1818 to connect Redding Canal with the River Neath near Cadoxton. This would bring down coal from George Tennant's Rhydings collieries to a shipping place on the river. Whether boats could be passed over this incline is not known.[10]

We now turn to water-operated counterbalancing inclines, a more successful variety. The best known canal employing these was the Morris Canal in the United States, the most ambitious and successful system of

28

inclines ever constructed. By an Act of the New Jersey Legislature dated 15 November 1822, commissioners were appointed to survey a route for a canal connecting the Delaware River to the Passaic River.[11] James Renwick (1792-1863), professor of natural philosophy and experimental chemistry at Columbia College, was appointed consulting engineer and Major Ephraim Beach resident engineer. Renwick, born in Liverpool,[12] and 'recognised as an authority in every branch of engineering' devised and patented a system of inclined planes for canals in 1823, and this was adopted on the Morris Canal. The size of the undertaking may be gauged by the fact that the summit level of the canal was 914 feet above mean tide at Newark N.J. on the Passaic River, and in the other direction 760 feet above low water in the Delaware River at Easton. The canal was 102 miles in length; on the East side of the summit level there were sixteen locks and twelve planes; on the West side, seven locks and eleven planes. The canal as originally constructed had a bottom width of twenty feet, top width of thirty-two feet and water depth of four feet. The locks were nine feet wide and seventy-five feet long. The original boats only carried a cargo of twenty-five tons and the locks had been made smaller than those on the Lehigh Canal from which cargoes of coal originated. In 1835-6 the length of canal boats was increased, and in 1845, by introducing sectional boats, which could be divided in the middle for passing locks and inclines, the capacity of each boat was raised to seventy tons.

The section or hinge boat had a total length of eighty-seven and a half feet, a width of ten-and-a-half feet and drew four-and-a-half feet loaded. It was made in two halves, as if the finished boat were cut through transversely and the open portions closed by flat vertical bulkheads. At the bulkheads the two sections were joined by metal fittings and pins, permitting vertical movement of the two halves. The maximum space between the two sections was seven inches. When the pins were removed, the two halves could be handled independently.

These boats worked over the eastern Pennsylvania canals, the Lehigh, Delaware Division and Delaware & Raritan, as well as the Morris Canal.[13]

According to David Stevenson[14] who visited the Morris Canal in 1837 in company with 'Mr.Douglass, the engineer for that work' − presumably David Bates Douglass (1790-1849) − the boats then in use on the canal were eight feet six inches broad, from sixty feet to eighty feet long and twenty-five to thirty tons burden. He shows the boat cars running on two four-wheeled bogies. According to him, the greatest weight ever drawn up the planes was about fifty tons. He felt that the great objection to the system was the damage caused to the boats by being carried dry over the inclines, but nevertheless he said that 'the twenty-three inclined planes on the Morris Canal are in full operation, and act remarkably well.'

The planes varied in height from thirty-five feet to 100 feet and from fifty feet to 150 feet in length, as follows:

Number	Name	Length	Type
Plane 11 west	Port Delaware	35 feet	single
Plane 10 west	nr Greenwich	44 feet	single
Plane 9 west	Port Warren	100 feet	double
Plane 8 west	Stewartsville	62 feet	single
Plane 7 west	Bowerstown	73 feet	single
Plane 6 west	Port Colden	50 feet	double
Plane 5 west	Port Murray	64 feet	single
Plane 4 west	Waterloo	80 feet	single
Plane 3 west	nr Lowrance's Landing	55 feet	single
Plane 2 west	Stanhope	70 feet	single
Plane 1 west	Port Morris	58 feet	single
Plane 1 east	Shipping Port	50 feet	single
Plane 2 east	Ledgewood	80 feet	single
Plane 3 east	Ledgewood	48 feet	single
Plane 4 east	Port Oram, later Wharton	52 feet	single
Plane 5 east	nr Dover	66 feet	single
Plane 6 east	Rockaway	52 feet	single
Plane 7 east	Boonton	80 feet	single
Plane 8 east	Montville	76 feet	single
Plane 9 east	Montville	74 feet	single
Plane 10 east	Beavertown, later Lincoln Park	56 feet	single
Plane 11 east	Bloomfield	54 feet	single
Plane 12 east	Newark, N.J.	70 feet	double

The planes were originally operated by waterwheels, later by reaction water turbines supplied with water by a wooden flume running from the top level and terminating in a 'plane house' occupied by the operator, where the water dropped through a vertical penstock to the turbine.[15] The turbines were of cast iron, with four adjustable nozzles; the water entered the nozzles from below, so that while working the weight of the wheel was lifted off the step bearing. The incline was laid with a twelve-and-a-half feet track on which an open-ended car ran. At the lower basin the car ran into the water, the boat was floated on, and an endless chain operated by the turbine took it up the incline. At the top the car either ran over a sill and down into the upper level, or into a lock. In the latter case, the gates were shut behind the boat and water admitted till the boat was on a level with the upper canal. The Boonton plane was the first to be completed, by December 1828. The first trip from Newark to Easton was completed on 4 November 1831. In 1835-6 all inclines of the sill type were altered to the lock type because of the increased length of the boats (no doubt they tended to dip into the top basin if they were too long). After 1845, on the introduction of sectional boats the inclines were all changed back to the sill type, the work being completed by 1860. The chains first used for hauling up the inclines were found to break frequently; there is a nice story of the Captain's wife on the boat *Electa* which ran away down the Boonton incline, bounced on the lower basin and was thrown over an embankment twenty feet high, landing in some trees. The good lady, who had her two children with her, 'allowed' that the boat went down 'right fast' but thought 'that that was the way the thing worked'. Chains were replaced by hempen rope, and after 1860 Roebling's steel wire ropes were introduced and used until the canal shut down. Only one operator was needed, and in his plane house he had an excellent view of the incline. The movement of the boat was controlled by a band brake applied by hand, with a brake drum eight feet in diameter. The difficulty of operating in foggy weather was overcome by the use of a geared indicator showing the operator the position of the car, similar to that used on colliery winding gear. To pass a boat took fifteen to twenty minutes at first, but after the introduction of section boats, it could take considerably longer if the job had to be done in two instalments. It appears that dividing boats was only done in unusual circumstances, as the introduction of sectional boats was coupled with the introduction of sectional cars, so that the boats could pass over the inclines in one operation. Another unexpected benefit of the inclines was that while the boats were on the cars, water could be drained from the bilges or running repairs — caulking, for example — could be carried out. Points of interest were at Plane 6 west, which incorporated a weighbridge or scale for weighing boats to establish their 'tare' weight, and at Plane 12 east, where a street crossed the canal plane and a crossing gate blocked the street when the plane was in use. An additional plane, inserted late in the history of the canal, is dealt with later as it was electrically operated.

Unfortunately the Morris Canal suffered at first from having been built to too small a section, and after it had been enlarged it encountered railroad competition. In 1844 it was sold by the mortgagees, a new company to work it being formed, and this company began an enlargement programme in 1845. The stockholders also invested heavily in the rival Delaware Division Canal Company, formed in 1858, and were able by controlling that company to divert traffic to the Morris Canal.[16] This brought the canal within sight of prosperity. Traffic was 58,259 tons in 1845 and 889,220 tons in 1866, when the company made its only profit.[17] In 1871 the Lehigh Valley Railroad, which had no other access to New Jersey or New York, leased the canal, and for a year or two worked the canal energetically. But the great drawback of all canals in the eastern United States was that all operations had to be suspended during the severe winters, when of course, coal was most needed. The water was then drained from the canal. By 1875 the Lehigh Valley Railroad had built a competing railway, and thereafter canal traffic declined. In 1923 the canal was taken over by the State and the following year it was abandoned. One of the water turbines was set up at Lake Hopatcong as a memorial to the canal company, by the consulting engineer, Colonel C.C. Vermeule. Many of the works can still be seen.[18] The Morris Canal system of inclines was well thought out and worked satisfactorily after the usual teething troubles, while the sectional boats proved successful. It influenced the design of canal inclines as far distant as East Prussia and Japan.

A pair of inclines, derived from the Morris Canal works, of which little was known until recently was put into service in the obscure Shubenacadie Canal in Nova Scotia, Canada.[19] This disastrous undertaking was intended to cross Nova Scotia from Dartmouth near Halifax to Port Eliot on the Bay of Fundy. The original scheme for boats drawing eight feet of water involved a rise of ninety-five feet ten inches from Dartmouth to the summit level at Shubenacadie Lake by eight locks, including a flight of five locks at Dartmouth. Work was started in 1826 but suspended for lack of money in 1831 and eventually a Committee of Investigation was established by the Legislature to deal with the problem. This Committee received a report on 13 February 1850 from Charles W. Fairbanks, C.E., which recommended the installation of three inclines, one at Dartmouth to replace the existing flight of five locks, another at Lock No. 6 to rise to the summit level and a third at Marshall's Inn to replace a descending flight of three locks. Fairbanks' report is a little puzzling since he refers to 'two lines of railways' later on in the report, although the detailed recommendations refer to three. He stated that he recommended them as being much cheaper than locks, and instanced the Morris Canal, which he had seen.

Fairbanks was appointed engineer to the new Inland Navigation Company formed to complete the canal, and work recommenced on 18 June 1854. In his 1855 report to the Company he stated that the incline at Portobello (formerly called Marshall's Inn) was graded and ready for the rails. It was to be about 600 feet long and to rise thirty-five feet. Water to work this incline, and the other incline at Dartmouth, was to be drawn from Lake Charles, the summit level. The inclined plane at Dartmouth, he reported, was to be about 1,500 feet long. This plane rose almost sixty feet and was inclined at one inch in twenty-two, the Portobello incline being one in sixteen.

A further Report for the Company was obtained on 19 May 1856 from an American Engineer, W.H. Talcott, who stated that he was in charge of the Morris Canal.[20] He was enthusiastic about the inclines, saying that they were to be similar to the Morris Canal ones and 'there need not therefore be any doubt or fear about the success of the inclined planes on your work'. He recommended the use of one-and-three-quarter inch ropes, rails of seventy-six pounds per yard, and the same type of turbine as used on the Morris Canal. The machinery for the inclines was provided by John F. Ward of Jersey City, U.S.A., and Mr. Grieg's Foundry in Dartmouth, N.S. On 19 February 1858 the Company asked for more money from the Legislature, reporting that the inclined plane at Marshall's Inn was completed and had been passed in both directions by a Steamer 'which is now seen resting in the cradle'. Finally, on 12 February 1862, a Minute of the Executive Council recorded that the navigation was completed. The Company almost immediately became insolvent and passed into the hands of new owners, the Lake & River Navigation Company. In 1870 the property was sold again, to L.P. Fairbanks, but shortly afterwards navigation was virtually stopped by a low fixed railway bridge being built across the Canal, and the works rapidly decayed. The boats using the inclines were sixty-six feet long, sixteen feet six inches wide and drew four feet of water. The reasons for the failure of the navigation being primarily commercial, there is little or no evidence available as to whether the inclines were technically successful; but as they were modelled on the Morris Canal inclines there seems to be no reason why they should not have worked satisfactorily. There is no doubt that in 1861 a vessel named the *Avery* made the round trip and that some timber and coal was moved through the canal between 1862 and 1870.

After describing so many canal inclines which have ceased to operate it is a pleasure to come to a group which originated in the 1840s, have survived political changes, two catastrophic wars and still continue to give good service. These are the inclines on what was formerly in East Prussia and known as the Elbing-Oberlandische Canal but is now in Poland and known as the Warmia or Elblag Canal (*Kanal Elblaski*).

Construction of this canal started on 28 October 1844 to connect the port of Elbing (now Elblag) through the Drausensee to two large lakes, the Geserichsee and Drewenzsee.[21] It is approximately 163 km. long. Originally there was a flight of locks connecting the Drausensee with the upper levels of the canal, and inland there were four inclines as follows:

Name	Vertical Height	Length
Buchwald	20.40 metres	224.80 metres
Kanten	18.83 metres	225.97 metres
Schonfeld	21.97 metres	262.63 metres
Hirschfeld	21.97 metres	263.63 metres

During construction it was realised that the number of conventional locks required would be large, and the use of inclined planes was suggested. Reports had been received of the success of the inclines on the Morris Canal, and the government engineer in charge of the works, Herr Steenke, was sent to America in 1850 to inspect the Morris Canal for himself. He returned with a report and sketches, but his superior, Herr Lentze, did not entirely approve of the mechanism of the American inclines and the machinery was redesigned. After a few minor adjustments it proved successful.

The canal works were built under the direction of Herr Steenke, as engineer in chief, and the machinery of the inclines was put in by Herr Kruger, the director of the Royal Machine Works at Dirschau, about twenty miles east of Elbing. The boats, which were not more than seventy-seven to eighty feet long, eight feet three inches to nine feet nine inches wide and drew not more than three feet three inches, ran up the inclines dry on a carriage which was supported on two four-wheeled bogies thirty feet apart. The bogies were capable of turning on a horizontal axis so as to adjust themselves to differences of slope. The gauge of the rails was approximately ten feet two inches. The total weight to be moved up or down an incline would be in the region of 105 tonnes, consisting of the carriage (twenty-five tonnes), the boat (ten tonnes) and the cargo (seventy tonnes). As well as boats, rafts of timber were carried on the inclines, timber being the great export of the country. Deck cargo was limited to not more than 2.80 metres (nine feet two inches) above the waterline.

Each incline is double, and the carriages are hauled by wire ropes, moved by pinions driven by waterwheels situated at the top of the inclines and at right angles to them, drawing water from the upper pound. The arrangement of the cables is that from the bottom of each incline the cable continues under water for some 100 yards before rising past one wheel, over a second at right angles, and back past a third (all three set in the middle of the canal) before returning to the other cradle. In the upper pound, cable wheels are set at some distance from the top, towards the side of the canal where the waterwheel is.[22] The speed on the incline is given as about one metre per second. The arrangements for lowering the boats into the top basin are similar to those on the Morris Canal.

So successful were these inclines that the canal or its equipment was modernised between 1874 and 1881, and about 1885, the five locks at the lower end of the canal were suppressed and replaced by a fifth incline. It is stated that whereas on the locks the passage of a boat took twenty minutes and consumed 1,000,000 gallons of water, on an incline seventy-two feet in height the passage took ten minutes and only 80,000 gallons of water.

In 1860 the waterwheels working the inclines were described as being twenty-seven fuss diameter, twelve fuss wide, with sixty buckets giving sixty-eight horsepower; water consumption when working at full power was thirty-four cubic fuss per second.[23]

The first trial of the Buchwald incline, which was perfectly successful, was on 31 August 1860. On 29 October 1860, the first canal boat laden with wood passed the inclined planes, and on the following day the first loaded boat reached Elbing.

According to recent official information[24] there are today the five inclines, now known as Caluny, Jelenie, Olesnica, Katy and Buczyniec, giving a total rise of ninety-nine metres in a distance of 9.2 km. The inclines, now known as 'Pochylnie', have been very sensibly kept working as a tourist attraction,[25] and there is a frequent passenger boat service. These are the only surviving water operated inclines and that they continue to work today must be a great tribute to the design and workmanship of Herr Steenke, Herr Kruger and their successors, and to the imagination of the present administration. Counterbalancing can be employed to economise on power but is not essential to operation.

Surprisingly, the last water powered incline to be dealt with was in Japan, on the Biwako Canal. This was built to connect Lake Biwa with Kyoto between 1885 and 1890, by direction of the governor of Kyoto, Kunimichi Kitagaki, not only for navigation but also to supply water to Kyoto City. The engineer in chief was a most remarkable man, Sakuro Tanabe

A.M.I.C.E. (1861-1944), who visited the U.S.A. in 1888-9 and included in his itinerary a visit to the Morris Canal. Tanabe also built Japan's first hydro-electric plant and became Professor of Civil Engineering at Kyoto University.[26]

The lower of two inclined planes on the canal was on the Kyoto-Fushimi section known as the Kamogawa Canal, built about 1894 in replacement of the earlier Takasegawa Canal; it was known as the Fushimi Incline. It was a double incline, operated by an endless cable attached to cradles on which the boats were carried. The endless cable was operated by a huge wooden drum in a high archway at the bottom of the incline, worked by water power. However, the incline was removed, possibly for road improvements, in about 1968. Unfortunately there is not very much information about this incline; the other incline on the Biwako Canal is dealt with later, being the first electrically operated canal incline.

That inclines operated by water power are not impractical in modern conditions is demonstrated by the survival of the Elblag Canal inclines, though these must be regarded as being more in the nature of a tourist attraction than a serious commercial enterprise. In the middle of last century, engineers realised that with the increasing scale of operations, some other form of power was desirable, especially since surplus water was not always available at inclines. Indeed, the absence of surplus water is in itself one of the reasons for preferring inclines or lifts to locks. The first form of prime mover to be tried was naturally enough steam.

The first full-scale canal incline to be worked by steam power was at the Blackhill locks on the Monkland Canal in Scotland[27], where the canal rose eighty feet. These locks had been put in about 1783, and doubled between 1837 and 1841 to increase the capacity of the canal, which conveyed large quantities of coal and iron into Glasgow. Trade increasing steadily, by 1849 the supply of water for the locks at Blackhill was running short. James Leslie, M.I.C.E., and J.F. Bateman (later la Trobe-Bateman) reported that extra supplies of water would be very difficult to obtain, and suggested either pumping up water from the bottom to the top of the flight of locks or installing an incline to handle the empty up-going traffic. The latter suggestion was adopted, and an incline (locally referred to as 'the gazoon') was designed by Leslie and completed by August 1850.

James Leslie, who was justifiably proud of this incline, read a paper on the subject to the Institute of Civil Engineers in 1853, the discussion of which contains much information about other inclines and lifts. The meeting was attended by such prominent engineers as G.P. Bidder, C.B. Vignoles and Joseph Cubitt. Leslie described the incline as having a vertical height of ninety-six feet, a length of 1,040 feet and a gradient of one in ten. There were two lines of rails, gauge seven feet, each having on it a carriage with a caisson. Although the incline was designed for returning empty boats upwards, counterbalancing was effected by the descending caisson being filled with water so nearly to equal the weight of the ascending caisson. Motion was imparted by two twenty-five horse power high pressure steam engines, driving two vertical drums on separate shafts in opposite directions, two-inch steel rope being coiled on the drums, which moved one turn to twelve strokes of the engine. These drums, sixteen feet in diameter, were in a pit under the top of the incline.

The caissons were seventy feet long by thirteen feet four inches wide by two feet nine inches, the cross section being from a mould of the standard boat, to save water. Each caisson had ten pairs of wheels, of which eight were three feet diameter, one pair two feet three inches and one pair one foot eight inches, the smaller wheels being at the top. In operation, a caisson was run down to the lower sluice and a boat admitted; the portcullis type gates were then shut and the caisson run up to the top, where it was pressed against the gates of the top reach by hydraulic rams. The gates were then lifted and the boat moved out. This process was remarkably quick, two minutes to enter the caisson, five or six to rise up the incline, and two minutes to move out at the top. In practice, sixteen boats could be passed in two hours; in April 1851 an average of fifty-one per day was achieved. Ratchet and pawl safety catches were fitted, and a 'traction spring' allowed the pawls to descend if there was a breakaway; a cast iron ratchet plate for the pawls to fall into was provided along the outside of each rail. In addition, a friction wheel was provided which would slip if unusual resistance was met. A self acting trigger was provided at the top, so that steam was cut off first half and then completely as a boat arrived. The only recorded accident was in Autumn 1851, when the spur wheel on the second drumshaft broke — even so, with only one side in action, they could pass thirty boats a day.

The incline was only intended to work during the six or seven months of the year when there was water shortage, but between 26 March 1853 and 3 September 1853 it passed 6,456 boats ascending and 184 descending. Between 1852 and 1856 the average in a season was 7,500 boats and in the best year 8,674 boats passed. According to Leslie, the waste of water on each passage was only fifty cubic feet, and the boilers used two and a quarter tons of refuse coal in a ten hour shift. Boats carried sixty tons cargo, the maximum weight on a trip being seventy to eighty tons.

In practice it was found that the water in the caissons caused violent oscillation, and the caissons had to be drained. The firm responsible for the machinery of this remarkable incline was Messrs. Yule & Wilkie.

Traffic on the Monkland Canal continued to rise until 1866, but it was taken over by the Caledonian Railway in the following year, and a steady falling off in trade occurred, as a result partly of railway competition and partly of the old coal pits being worked out. The incline was finally closed as unnecessary about 1887[28] and the machinery has been cleared away though the site can still be seen.

The last steam-worked incline to be built was at Foxton on the Grand Union Canal, which had been taken over by the Grand Junction Canal Co in 1894.[29] The new owners were most anxious to develop traffic from the Derbyshire Coalfields to London, spurred on by the leading firm of canal hauliers, Messrs. Fellows Morton & Clayton. This company wished to operate wide (fourteen feet) boats over the section but this was impossible owing to the existence of flights of narrow (seven feet) locks at Foxton and at Watford, Northamptonshire.[30] The Foxton Locks in particular, consumed a great deal of time and water. In 1894 Barnabas James Thomas and Joseph Jex Taylor, civil engineers of London, sent to Gordon Thomas, the engineer of the Grand Junction Company, who was a cousin of B.J. Thomas, a plan for an inclined plane; and this grew into a scheme patented by all three, Patent No. 8504 of 1896. Two models were made in 1896,[31] the second a large scale working model at Bulbourne works, and following these tests the Grand Junction Canal Company bought land at Foxton in 1897 and asked for tenders for construction of the incline. J. & H. Gwynne of Hammersmith obtained the contract and the incline was officially opened on 10 July 1900.

The incline was undoubtedly a fine conception, and the principle adopted of lowering the boats transversely, has recently been followed on a French canal. The arrangement was of two huge caissons or steel tanks, having sixteen wheels in pairs running on four steel rails. They were placed slightly *en echelon* so that boats going into the far caisson at the top could pass behind the near caisson, and vice versa at the bottom. The wheels were so arranged that the caissons were always horizontal, and the longitudinal arrangement avoided the need for a sill at the top. The tanks were eighty feet long by fifteen feet wide and five feet deep, and could hold two narrow boats or one wide boat. Counterbalancing was employed, one caisson being always at the top when the other was at the bottom. The caissons were fitted with lifting guillotine type gates at each end, and at the top hydraulic rams were used to press the caisson against the end of the upper basin of the canal, which also had a guillotine type gate. When pressed together the two gates could be lifted, allowing the boats to pass in and out of the caisson. The tanks being full of water were the same weight whether or not they were occupied by boats, and by slightly altering the slope of each incline at the top to counteract the loss of weight of the descending caisson as it entered the water, the need for additional power was kept to a minimum. A twenty-five horse power steam engine was provided to raise and lower the caissons and also to provide the hydraulic power for operating the gates and the rams.

The positioning of the incline, to the east of the Foxton locks and more or less at right angles, has been criticised. There must have been good reasons for this, but the site involved the building up of the top end of the incline. As a result the civil engineering works cost double the estimate, and included putting supports for the rails of the incline down to bed rock. When completed and tested, on 11 July 1900, the incline worked satisfactorily, but as usual with new departures in engineering there proved to be a weak point. In the case of the Foxton incline this was the size of the rails supporting the tanks, which were not nearly heavy enough, and developed an alarming habit of curling up under load. Once heavier section rails were installed, the mechanism appears to have been quite satisfactory and the maintenance costs remarkably low. The figure given for cost of operation is so low (even granted the cost of labour and coal in those days) that it can hardly have included any figure for depreciation. One interesting point is that no trouble seems to have been experienced with surging of the water in the tanks. Surging is not likely to be experienced as much in a transverse plane as in a longitudinal plane such as Blackhill, but Thomas's design did provide for cushioning of the pull when starting a movement.

The incline certainly saved a great deal of water passing from the summit level of the canal in a northward direction, and it passed boats in twelve minutes – to pass the flight of locks took eighty minutes.

However, the Board of the Grand Junction Canal, after some hesitation, had the flight of locks at Watford rebuilt as narrow locks, which effectively negated the advantage of having built the incline to accommodate wide boats. This does lend some colour to the opinion which has been expressed, that the Board's real purpose in building the incline was to minimise the water flowing North out of the Grand Union Canal, so that more would be available for the Grand Junction Canal at the south end of the Grand Union. But this is to venture on matters of policy not likely to be expressed in writing, and the fact remains that the anticipated traffic from Derbyshire failed to materialise, and consequently the Grand Junction did not exercise its option to buy the Leicester, Loughborough and Erewash Canals. The incline became a white elephant, and on the 26 October 1910 a fortnight's notice of closure was given. Apparently it did work occasionally after this date, but the machinery was sold for scrap in 1928. The chief mechanical troubles had been the breaking of the rails and the cracking of the hydraulic cylinders in frosty weather. Many motorists will sympathise with the employee who was carpeted in 1909 for failure to put enough antifreeze in the system.[32]

The failure of the Foxton Incline was assured from the commercial point of view by the failure to widen the locks at Watford, and also by the use of steam power, which required constant attendance. It is unfair to blame the Thomases for using steam in the late 1890s; but Dr. Sakuro Tanabe had already constructed an incline powered by hydro-electricity in about 1890 in Japan.

On the upper part of the Biwako Canal, on the eastern edge of Kyoto city, Dr. Tanabe built an incline with a drop of 118 feet having a slope of one in fifteen, and a length of 1,815 feet.[33] The boats travelled on cradles mounted on two four-wheeled bogies, open ended and made of steel girders. Locks on the canal were constructed to accommodate boats forty-seven-and-a-half feet long, seven-and-a-half feet wide and four feet draft, and the cradles appear to have been able to carry the same. The operation of this incline, which was counterbalancing, was by hydro-electric power from a Sprague electric motor, fifty horse power, 440 volts, which worked a drum on which the four-inch steel rope attached to the cradles was wound. Power was supplied from dynamos worked by two

Pelton wheels driven by water taken from the upper reach of the canal. As the canal came from Lake Biwa, which is Japan's largest fresh water lake, there was plenty of water always available.

Unfortunately, though Dr. Tanabe wrote a book on the canal which was published in Kyoto in 1940,[34] no-one has yet translated it from Japanese, so that a full length account of this remarkable canal is not available in English. As far as can be discovered, however, commercial operations ceased in 1914.[35] The Kyoto incline is still in existence, together with its cradles, but the wire rope has been removed. Perhaps a Japanese equivalent of the Ironbridge Gorge Museum will take it in hand and set it to work again some day.

An electrically powered incline which was built, maintained and operated by a railroad company, the Delaware Lackawanna & Western, was put in at Orange Street, Newark, N.J., to enable the rails to go under rather than over the Morris Canal. Originally the canal had passed under the railroad, but when it was decided to lower the rail level by five feet it was realised that this would stop navigation. The problem was solved by installing an electrically driven incline or hump to carry boats on the usual Morris Canal car across the rails while 'the canal water flowed through an inverted syphon from one section of the canal to the other'.[36] The date when this was done is not recorded.

Hydro-electricity has also been used in a small installation in Canada where the Trent Canal system forms 'an improved natural waterway connecting Lake Ontario and Georgian Bay'[37] on Lake Huron. It was originally intended for transport of lumber and freight, but is now almost exclusively used by pleasure traffic.

At the Georgian Bay end the Severn River was regulated for navigation by two dams, at Swift Rapids and Big Chute. Here were placed two inclines, confusingly styled 'marine railways'. These were single-line electrically operated installations, and were built 'as a temporary expedient in lieu of three locks, the construction of which was stopped in 1916 due to wartime conditions.'[38] It appears that these marine railways were opened for traffic in 1919. They would take boats not exceeding sixty feet long, thirteen feet six inches in width and drawing not more than four feet of water. The marine railways prevented large boats using the system as a through way, as from Lake Ontario to Swift Rapids the system was open to vessels 134 feet by thirty-three feet and drawing six feet of water.[39] The Swift Rapids marine railway carried vessels over a vertical height of forty-seven feet and the Big Chute over a vertical height of fifty-eight feet. The motive power was an electrically operated winch housed in a wooden building at the top of the incline. Boats were run onto a small railway truck with open ends, fitted with moveable saddle pads which were forced up against the bilge of the boat by means of threaded screw rods. The truck was then hauled out of the water up a gentle slope, over the sill and down the other side of the incline, which fell at an angle of 30°. The cable from the winch passed through a set of sheaves in front of the building, and when the truck passed this point the strain on the cable was transferred from the sheave on the up-coming side to the sheave on the down-going side.[40] One disadvantage was that there was a distinct slope on a boat while going down the long side of the incline and the contents tended to slip down to the lower end. The Swift Rapids Marine Railway was replaced in 1965 by a modern chamber lock with a lift of forty-five feet but in 1973 the Big Chute Marine Railway was still in active operation, and the only place in the world where a road and a canal had a level crossing.[41] At the top end a road crossed the canal between the rails leaving the water of the upper pound and reaching the sill. As the original Marine Railway could not take any vessel of more than twenty tons, a larger improved version was installed in the summer of 1978 to carry boats of a maximum displacement of 100 tons, a length of 100 feet, draft of six feet and beam of twenty-four feet. The boats are carried dry, supported on slings manipulated by hydraulic cylinders, and by the use of tracks at different levels the carriage remains on an even keel while in transit. Power is provided by four one hundred horse power electric winches. Thus the ecological danger of sea-lampreys penetrating the Trent Canal system from Lake Huron has been avoided.[42]

On the Angara River in Siberia at the Bugachany hydro-electric plant, the dam causes a seventy metre difference in levels and rafts are passed over this on a three-section electrically driven platform running on rails on a gradient of one in twenty-five at a speed of 220 metres per minute, the transit from one reach to the other taking about twenty-six minutes. Timber being virtually the only traffic the rafts are hauled dry over the ramp and no attempt seems to be made to keep the load horizontal.[43]

CHAPTER V

THE MODERN CANAL INCLINE – PROGRESS SINCE 1950

After 1900 the designing of canal inclines lapsed in Europe for fifty years – indeed informal correspondence from an official source in France in 1950 indicates that at that date the French at least considered both lifts and inclines out of date, favouring high-rise locks.[1] Since 1950 the movement to modernise and enlarge the canal system of Northern Europe has led to a revival of interest in inclines, particularly where flights of locks require to be dispensed with in the interests of saving both time and water. The great increase in size of canal craft in Europe has apparently led to difficulties in designing high-rise locks without raising problems of scouring and turbulence. In modern canal building primary emphasis has changed from the saving of water to the saving of time and space, and in large modern canals the incline can still find a place. As Hirsch pointed out, carrying boats dry as was the practice on early inclines, is only suitable for canals of local significance using boats built specially for the purpose.[2] Large modern craft require to be kept afloat on inclines, but modern designers have been successful in allowing for this.

In the early 1950s, the Ministry of Public Works and Reconstruction in Belgium proposed the enlargement of the Charleroi-Brussels Canal to carry 1,350 tonne instead of 300 tonne barges.[3] The canal then existing rose by eleven locks from Charleroi to the summit level, and then fell by no less than twenty-seven locks towards Brussels. At Charleroi it connected with the Belgian Canal du Centre with its four hydraulic lifts.

The plan for the enlarged canal necessitated cutting down the summit level and lengthening it from eleven to twenty-eight kilometres; three locks replaced the eleven on the Charleroi side of the summit level and an incline at Ronquières and seven other locks replaced the twenty-seven on the Brussels side. Between Seneffe and Ronquières the existing canal fell by fourteen locks, which were to be rendered unnecessary by some twelve kilometres of new canal and a fall of 67.55 metres at Ronquières. Plans for achieving this were narrowed down to either a single vertical lift, or a single inclined plane of a longitudinal type. Mainly on geological grounds – the presence of suitable rocky subsoil conditions – it was decided to instal an inclined plane of a five per cent slope. A two per cent slope was also considered and rejected. After careful planning in the State Hydraulic

Laboratories, assisted by large models, work started on the construction of the incline on 15 March 1962.[4]

At the head of the 'sloping lock' or inclined plane the upper canal is carried on a bridge construction for 300 metres. The incline is 1,432 metres long, and has a tower 125 metres high at the upper end and one forty metres high at the lower end. The two metal caissons which can be worked together or separately and are not counterbalanced by each other but by counterweights, are ninety-one metres long by twelve metres wide, and hold water varying in depth from three metres to 3.7 metres according to the level in the upper reach. Each caisson can carry either one 1,350 tonne barge or four 300 tonne barges, and runs on no less than 236 rollers of seventy centimetres diameter; a caisson weighs from 5,000 to 5,700 tonnes and the counterweights, which run on 192 rollers in a trough under each caisson, weigh 5,200 tonnes. Each caisson is operated by four cables fifty-five millimetres in diameter running over a drum designed to grip the cables and avoid slipping. Power is supplied by six electric motors developing more than one thousand horse power. Electricity is supplied from the mains, with a standby hydro-electric station in case of failure. A system of flywheels ensures that in case of an electrical breakdown a caisson will come to a gradual stop. At the top and bottom of the incline the caissons are pressed against the gates of the canal by hydraulic pressure. The movements are controlled by a control room in the tower at the upper end, including a system of supervision by closed-circuit television, and electric interlocking to prevent errors in operation. Tourists are catered for by a lift which takes them to the top of the upper tower where there is an observation room.

Construction of this incline, which was carried out by a consortium of Belgian contracting companies, did not proceed without difficulty — in 1964 trouble was encountered with unsatisfactory subsoil conditions,[5] — but the incline was opened to traffic in 1968. The engineer in chief was M. Gustave Willems, Secretary General of the Ministry of Public Works & Reconstruction, and Professor at the Free University of Brussels. It is interesting that Professor Willems evidently regards his plane as being derived from the Blackhill incline. He seems to have overcome the difficulty of 'surging' of water in the caissons which was encountered at Blackhill. Unfortunately the hopes of greatly increased traffic following the installation of the Ronquières incline have not been fulfilled. Traffic surveys had suggested that the traffic should double in ten years but this has not happened, partly due to subsidised rail competition and partly due to other structures on the canal between Brussels and Ronquières not being of the standard dimensions for the 1350-tonne barges. In addition certain parts of the machinery, notably the caisson wheelsets, have worn more rapidly than anticipated. Nevertheless the incline makes possible substantial savings in transport costs even when only passing 300-tonne barges.[6]

In 1957 French engineers of the Service of Bridges and Roads were considering the improvement of the Marne-Rhine Canal which fell to the east from its summit level in the Vosges mountains near St Louis-Arzviller, by a series of eighteen locks of 2.60 metres each in a total length of 3.940 kilometres.[7] Negotiating these was a lengthy business and prodigal of water, aggravated by the relative shortness of some of the intermediate reaches of the canal. The problems were made worse by the simultaneous presence of the canal, a trunk road, and the Paris-Strasbourg railway line in one narrow valley, leaving little room for manoeuvre. After considering various schemes it was decided to build a new line of canal on the hillside above the road, down to the south east end of the string of locks, where the hillside opens out sufficiently to allow a transverse inclined plane to be built. The transverse arrangement permits the slope to be steeper than a longitudinal incline and in fact the slope at St Louis-Arzviller is 41°.

The administration of the canal having called for competitive schemes, two consortia of civil engineering contractors submitted plans for transverse inclines, and the administration decided to select the best features of each and invite the rivals to unite in carrying out the work.

The scheme was to cover a vertical fall of 44.55 metres by an incline 108.65 metres in length. There were to be two caissons, one behind the other, not *en echelon* as at Foxton; and like the Belgian incline the caissons were to be counterbalanced by counterweights running between the rails which supported the caissons. The caissons could run independently of each other, or coupled together if required. At a maximum speed of 0.60 metres per second on the incline, it was calculated that with one caisson in use, nineteen boats could be passed one way and twenty the other in a thirteen hour day, while with two in use, thirty-eight boats could be passed one way and forty the other.

As the latter figures apparently exceed the capacity of the rest of the canal it was finally decided to proceed with a single caisson only, while laying out the works in such a way that a second caisson could be added reasonably soon. No less than seventeen locks are replaced by the incline.[8]

The caisson runs on two double lines of track, 0.80 metres wide, the gauge overall being 25.7 metres. Underneath the caisson is the counterweight twenty-two metres wide, running on similar double rails with a gauge overall of 10.40 metres. The cables holding the caisson and counterweight run over the drums at the top which are driven by electricity. The interior of the caisson measures 42.50 metres by 5.50 metres by 3.20 metres and each caisson or counterweight has thirty-two wheels arranged in eight four-wheeled bogies. At each end of the caisson is a lifting gate which buts up against a similar gate at the end of the canal, both gates being raised and lowered simultaneously.

This incline, as at Ronquières, carries the barges afloat in the caissons, but problems of surging were not considered to be likely to be troublesome as the plane is transverse, and the circumstances of a partial load (i.e. where instead of four 350 tonne barges in a caisson there are only one, two or three) cannot occur at St Louis-Arzviller. The weight of the caisson varies between 868 tonnes and 939 tonnes when filled with water.

43

At both Ronquières and St Louis-Arzviller it is worth noting that precautions against frost damage have been taken, particularly to guard against the gates being frozen up.

Two men are required to operate the incline, one at the control panel and one on the caisson. Numerous safety devices have been incorporated in the design.

The work was authorised in 1964, and the incline was commissioned on the 27 January 1969. By the end of November, 5,400 barges had passed the incline. It is found that in practice maintenance of the incline calls for it to be taken out of service from time to time, and the line of locks will not be dismantled until the second caisson has been added to the incline. One encouraging feature of the incline in operation is that the oscillations of the water level in the caisson have been found to be so slight that they may be ignored.

During the technical studies which preceded the building of the St Louis-Arzviller incline, a revolutionary proposal was put forward which was rejected for use there with reluctance, particularly because it was felt that it 'could constitute a specifically national (i.e French) solution of the spanning of high falls, just as the principle of the boat lift is applied by the Germans and that of the inclined plane by the Belgians'.[9]

M. Aubert, Inspector General of Bridges and Roads, and M. Bouchet, an engineer in the service of the Strasbourg Navigation, devised the idea of a 'water slope'.[10] This is a concrete flume connecting the upper and lower reaches of the canal with a road bed on either side of which run two diesel electric locomotives connected at the downstream end by a heavy beam. Towards the upstream end of the locomotives is a lighter girder carrying the 'shield' which has sides and bottom so designed as to seal the concrete flume. At the top of the concrete flume is a lifting gate which acts as a stop.

The method of working the water slope (assuming a barge to be proceeding upwards) is to run the barge between the locomotives, which are then at the bottom of the slope, into a slightly deepened portion of canal from which the concrete flume rises directly. The shield is lowered behind the barge, which is left floating in the water cut off by the shield from the lower canal. The locomotives then proceed to push the barge, which rests against a shock absorber on the front of the shield, up the concrete flume till it reaches the top and the level of water surrounding the barge equals the level of water in the upper canal. The gate of the upper canal is then opened and the barge passes through into the upper canal. Coming down, water is let into the space between the upper canal and the shield, if necessary, to equalize the water on each side of the gate. The gate is then raised and the barge passes through to rest against the shield. The gate then falls, cutting off the upper canal, and the locomotives come down the slope bringing the barge, in its water, behind the shield; on arrival in the basin at the bottom of the slope the shield is raised and the barge proceeds down the lower canal.

This really brilliant idea obviously depends on the reliability of modern materials, and in particular the means of sealing the shield in the flume so that water will not just leak out and leave the barge stranded half way down the slope. Considerable experimental work was carried out, firstly on a one fiftieth scale at the Chatou Laboratory, then in 1967 on a one tenth scale trial at Venissieux near Lyons and finally a full size waterslope was put in at Montech, between Toulouse and Agen on the Canal Lateral à la Garonne.[11]

Here it had been decided to rebuild the canal locks to pass barges 38.5 metres long and five metres wide, capable of carrying between 350 and 400 tonnes. At Montech locks eleven to fifteen have been replaced by a single waterslope six metres wide and forty metres long with a gradient of one in wazterslope six metres wide and forty metres long with a gradient of one in thirty-three. The two diesel electric locomotives are carried on extra heavy duty pneumatic tyres, which have apparently been chosen in preference to flanged wheels on normal railway track to avoid problems caused by slipping of the wheels, the two locomotives being synchronised electrically. The vertical rise is just over 13.3 metres and the weight to be lifted is calculated as being approximately 1,750 tonnes. At the top the slope meets a new portion of canal 800 metres long. Each of the locomotives is carried on four axles and their combined tare is 200 tonnes. Their speed when climbing is about 4.5 kilometres per hour, and a traverse takes only seven minutes.

This waterslope was finished at the end of 1972 and is being tested to ascertain its capabilities, and to assess the possibility of enlarging the system to deal with vertical falls of up to fifty metres and vessels of up to 4,000 tonnes. It was constructed by SPIE Batignolles under the supervision of the French Ministry of Equipment, Navigation Service, Midi Garonne.

Finally, there is a remarkable inclined plane in Siberia, on the River Yenisei at Krasnoyarsk (where the river is stated to be ice free for 196 days in the year).[12] This incline[13] operates over a vertical difference in level of 101 metres and has been designed to surmount the dam of a hydro-electric station; seventy-five per cent of the traffic consists of timber, which is intended to be worked over the incline in the first place in rafts and later in vessels of 1,500 tonnes. The remarkable feature of this incline is a turntable in the middle of the incline, the angle between the upper and lower tracks of the incline being 142°. The upper track is 500 metres long, the turntable is 103 metres or 106 metres in diameter and the lower track is 1,250 metres long, the optimum slope of the track being one in ten. Some sources give the difference in level as ninety-eight metres and the slope one in twelve.[14]

The caisson in which the vessels travel is intended to carry them afloat, it is designed for vessels of up to 1,500 tonnes but vessels of up to 2,000 tonnes can be accommodated. The weight of the caisson is 3,100 tonnes, light, or 6,700 tonnes with water. The caisson travels on 148 wheels forming seventy-four 'balancing carriers',[15] and there are arrangements for ensuring the even spread of the load over all wheels if the track is uneven. The design provides for an hydraulic drive consisting of 148 'hydromotors' (one for each wheel) driving on two racks on each rail. The gauge of the rails is nine metres. The caisson rises at sixty metres per minute and falls at eighty metres per minute. The turntable is an inclined welded bridge, resting on circular rail tracks at the circumference and on a giant circular roll-train, diameter 6.5 metres, at the centre. The centre abutment is designed to bear 6,500 tonne loads and rotates on fifty-five cone roller bearings. A repair platform near the turntable is intended to create a dead end siding so that the capacity of the incline can be increased; the present design can deal with up to fifteen round trips ('cycles') a day, each cycle lasting ninety-three minutes. The incline had not been completed in 1965 but it is now in operation.

It is obvious therefore that the canal incline is very much a living and developing mechanism, the recent designs of longitudinal and transverse inclines and water slopes offering variations of design to suit a variety of geological and economic situations.

PART II

CHAPTER VI

PORTAGE RAILWAYS AND SHIP RAILWAYS

The idea of transporting ships across from one sea to another can be traced in many places, by reference to place names and to literary sources. The name 'Tarbert' meaning 'launch the boat' occurs in several places in Scotland where a narrow neck of land joins two areas of water, enabling boats to be hauled out of the water on one side and manhandled across to the other.[1] It also appears that in England there are a number of places which derive their name from the Old English *draeg* (pl *dragu*)[2], indicating the existence of a portage in early medieval times; among these places are Drax in the West Riding (a portage between the Ouse and the Aire), Drayton near Farlington in Hampshire and also East and West Drayton in Nottingham-shire, which lie at the ends of a portage between tributaries of the Trent and the Idle.[3] One need not suppose that any boats carried over these would be particularly large, in fact a trip between East and West Drayton dragging or carrying any boat would be hard work, even if there were the Anglo-Saxon equivalent of licensed premises along the route.

There are a number of instances of the use of wooden inclines in military operations to enable boats to be pulled by manpower or by oxen over necks of land to outflank enemy positions. The best known are probably the occasions on which the Ottoman Turks employed such a stratagem. Firstly, on the night of 21-22 April 1453, during the siege of Constantinople, Mohammed the Conqueror passed a fleet of ships on cradles over a 'corduroy' track about 2,500 yards long behind Galata from Tophane to Kassim Pasha, so that it could be launched on the Golden Horn.

> The cradles were lowered into the water and the ships tied onto them there: then pulleys dragged them ashore and teams of oxen were harnessed in front of each, with teams of men to help over the steeper and more difficult parts of the road. In every boat the oarsmen sat in their places moving their oars in the empty air while the officers walked up and down giving the beat. Sails were hoisted exactly as though the vessels were at sea. Flags were flown, drums beaten and fifes and trumpets played while ship after ship was hauled up the hill, as it were in a fantastic carnival.[4]

This is often considered to have been the decisive move which led to the fall of Constantinople a few weeks later.

Eighty ships of the fleet of Mohammed's descendant, Soleyman the Magnificent, were dragged on wooden rollers from Marsamuscetto Creek to the upper end of Grand Harbour in Malta in late June 1565 during the Great Siege.[5] This enabled the besiegers to attack the defences of the Knights of Malta on all sides.

However, the arts of peace have provided the supreme example of boats being carried over mountains, on the celebrated Alleghany Portage Railroad in the United States.[6]

On 25 February 1826, the State Legislature in Philadelphia passed an Act providing for the construction at the expense of the State of a canal to open easy communications with Ohio, on the other side of the Alleghany Mountains. The original idea was to tunnel under the mountains, but the prospect of excavating a tunnel four-and-a half-miles long proved too much for the projectors and the final form which the Pennsylvania Canal Main Line took was a railroad from Philadelphia to Columbia, canal from Columbia to Holidaysburg, the Alleghany Portage Railroad from Holidaysburg to Johnstown, Pa., and a canal from Johnstown to Pittsburg. The construction of the Portage Railroad was authorised by an Act of 21 March 1831 and the work was carried out under Sylvester Welch as chief engineer [7] and Moncure Robinson as consultant. The railroad rose from Johnstown by five inclined planes to the summit at Summit House and then fell by another five planes to Holidaysburg.

The gauge of the railway was four feet nine inches and the edge rails were made by Harford Davis & Company in Wales as no American maker could produce the requisite quantity in the time allotted. The inclines were worked by winding engines though arrangements were made for counter-balancing where possible. The Portage Railroad was open for single track working on 18 March 1834 and for double track on 10 May 1835. Operations on the canal system generally were suspended from December to March on account of the severe winters.

The Portage Railroad became of particular interest to canal historians, and qualified for mention in a work on canal inclines, by events in October 1834, when—

> this portage was actually the means of connecting the waters of Eastern Pennsylvania with those of Mississippi; and, as the circumstance is peculiarly interesting, we here place it on record. Jess Chrisman, from the Lackawanna, a tributary of the north branch of the Susquehanna, loaded his boat named *Hit or Miss* with his wife, children, beds and family accommodation, pigeons and other live stock, and started for Illinois. At Holidaysburg, where he expected to sell his boat, it was suggested by John Dougherty, of the Reliance Transportation Line, that the whole concern could be safely hoisted over the mountain and

set afloat again in the canal. Mr. Dougherty prepared a railroad car calculated to bear the novel burden. The boat was taken from its proper element and placed on wheels, and under the superintendence of Major C. Williams (who, be it remembered, was the first man who ran a boat over the Alleghany Mountain) the boat and cargo at noon on the same day began their progress over the rugged Alleghany. All this was done without disturbing the family arrangements of cooking, sleeping, etc. They rested at night on the top of the mountain, like Noah's Ark on Ararat, and descended the next morning into the Valley of the Mississippi and sailed for St. Louis.[8]

At that time only horses were used for traction on the levels, but later locomotives were introduced, and horsepower finally disappeared at the end of the 1850 season.

In 1842, the Board of Canal Commissioners let contracts for eighteen sets of trucks of four sections each for the purpose of hauling sectional boats of a similar nature to those on the Morris Canal, with their cargoes, over the State Railroad — ten sets were placed on the Portage Railroad before the season opened in 1843, and to make them available boat planes leading from the basins at Holidaysburg and Johnstown were constructed. These sets of trucks were exceedingly successful, according to the management, and greatly increased the trade on the State system. In fact they were so popular that the private hauliers made strenuous efforts in the courts to force the Board to raise the tolls paid on section boats using the trucks. These efforts were fruitless, but the system became less successful as time went on. The original trucks were found to be too light in construction and frequently broke down under the increasing weight of boats and freight, damaging the track. In 1847, this led to the construction of heavier and stronger trucks. Whether these in turn were found to be too heavy for the road is not clear, but at the end of 1854 the Board reported that there were only seventeen sets of trucks, many of which required repair, that this number was considered sufficient and that in fact they had become a drawback on the revenue and consideration should be given to discouraging them. However, as will be explained, before the next season the old Portage Railroad was closed.

It is not altogether surprising that the planes on the railroad were not satisfactory. For one thing the original ropes (up to seven inches in diameter) were not capable of standing up to the wear on them for long before they needed replacement — and breakages were frequent — but the time consumed in attaching trains to the ropes, detaching them, and again attaching them to the locomotive for the following level stretch was enormous. In 1836, the Legislature of Pennsylvania authorised a survey of a route which would eliminate the inclines. However, the planes provided a great deal of employment and under the 'spoils system' afforded great opportunities for patronage by the political party for the time being in power, so that the proposal for their abolition was not welcomed in political circles. Nothing was done apart from replacing the ropes on the inclines by

Roebling's wire ropes, till 1850, when the threat of competition by the Pennsylvania Railroad and the decrepit state of the Old Portage Railroad, caused the Legislature to authorise the New Portage Railroad, to run through Sugar Run Gap. Work commenced in 1853 and was completed sufficiently to enable the Old Portage Railroad to be abandoned, on 1 July 1855. Alas, the Legislature, alarmed by the withdrawal of the business formerly put on the route by the Pennsylvania Railroad, had already passed an act authorising the sale of the main line including the Alleghany Portage Railroad. The entire works were bought in 1857 by the only bidder, the Pennsylvania Railroad, which closed the New Portage Railroad at the end of the season.

At the East end of the Pennsylvania Canal on the Susquehanna River there was a rail connection known as the Philadelphia & Columbia Railroad, on which the traffic was mainly horsedrawn. This had two inclines, the Belmont Plane at the east end, 2,805 feet long and rising 187 feet from the west bank of ¸the Schuylkill River several miles from Philadelphia, and at the west end the Columbia plane which lowered the cars to the canal level, 1,800 feet long and falling ninety feet. Both inclines were worked by stationary steam engines. This railway was opened on 15 April 1834 and was taken over and rebuilt by the Pennsylvania Railroad in 1857. Sectional canal boats were hauled over the two inclines.[9]

Another railway over which boats were carried was a remarkable installation at Normanton, West Yorkshire.[10] This was a standard gauge industrial railway which connected the colliery screens at St Johns Colliery to the Aire & Calder Navigation at Stanley Ferry. In 1862 William H. Bartholomew, the extremely enterprising engineer of the Aire & Calder Navigation, devised iron compartment boats − a development of the tub boat of Shropshire − twenty feet by fifteen feet and carrying twenty-five tons, which were joined together in trains and pushed − later pulled − by steam tugs. On arrival at Goole the compartment boats were uncoupled and moved into a tipper, which hoisted them into the air and tipped them over to shoot their contents into coasting vessels.[11]

In 1891, Locke & Company of St Johns Colliery thought of hauling the compartment boats onto railway flat waggons at Stanley Ferry and taking them by rail to the colliery for loading. This proved most successful, and the canal basin was enlarged in 1897. According to a diagram the system of working was that on arrival at Stanley Ferry from the colliery, the locomotive detached itself from the truck carrying the compartment boat at a slope towards the canal, and a rope was attached to the truck, run round a pulley and back to the locomotive. The brakes on the truck were then released and the weight of the load carried the truck down into the water, the locomotive serving as a brake. The loaded boat floated off the truck and an empty boat floated on; the locomotive then returned, hauled the truck out of the water by the rope round the pulley, coupled up and moved off to the colliery.[12] Unfortunately about 1941 new screens were installed at the colliery and for some reason were so designed that they did not accommodate the compartment boats, which had to remain at the basin and be loaded from a gantry.

In 1961 there existed a means of transferring boats not exceeding two tonnes in weight from the Swedish Dalsland Canal at Lake Stora Le on the Swedish-Norwegian border onto the Otteid arm of the Norwegian Tiste Canal. At Otteid there was a wharf with a crane which could lift a small boat from the lake onto a trolley which could be wound up the hillside on rails to the basin of the Norwegian canal. I have not yet discovered whether this can still be done, but it would be worth going to find out as Lake Stora Le is described as breathtakingly beautiful.[13]

Two other schemes were put forward during the latter part of the nineteenth century for building ship railways, one of which actually got to the stage of construction. The more ambitious scheme was for a ship railway across the Isthmus of Tehuantepec in Mexico, to connect the Atlantic and Pacific.[14] The distance between the two oceans at this point is approximately 125 miles and the height of the continental divide 735 feet (at Panama the distance is thirty-five miles in a straight line and the height 300 feet) but from the commercial point of view a crossing at Tehuantepec had attractions. After it had been found that an inter-oceanic canal was impossibly expensive, James Buchanan Eads (1820-1887) put forward a scheme for a ship railway in 1880-1. He had a great reputation as a civil engineer having done much work on improving the mouth of the Mississippi for navigation, and built the great bridge over the Mississippi at St Louis. He proposed a quadruple ship railway with caissons containing the ships, similar in general design to the Georgetown incline. The vision of sea-going ships being conveyed over 125 miles in 'a tank of water' running on rails stirred up a great deal of comment. Much of the most damaging criticism did in fact come from persons who had experience of the deficiencies of the Georgetown incline, in particular the problems of maintaining an even roadbed and of weight distribution. Eads seems to have thought that the Georgetown incline caisson was worked with water seven feet deep in it, whereas in practice it had to be worked dry, or with only twenty inches of water in it to reduce the weight on the rails and surging of the water. It appears from the critique of the scheme that even Hutton, the designer of the Georgetown incline, agreed that 'no comparison can be made between that work (the incline) and his (Eads') project'. In spite of wide publicity and numerous artists' impressions of steamships being drawn overland by railway locomotives, Eads' scheme failed to impress the Mexican Government, which let a contract in 1882 for the construction of a conventional railway across the Isthmus; this was finished in 1894 and almost immediately found inadequate.[15]

The second scheme was the Chignecto Marine Transport Railway, which was intended as a ship railway across the Chignecto Isthmus, to connect the Bay of Fundy to the Northumberland Strait and the Gulf of St Lawrence. Originally a canal was proposed, but about 1882 a scheme for a ship railway was put forward by H.G.C. Ketchum (1839-1896). This envisaged a railway across the Isthmus from Cumberland Basin to Baie Verte, with one of Edwin Clark's hydraulic lifts at each end to overcome the difficulties connected with the tidal range of up to sixty feet in the Bay of Fundy. The Chignecto Marine Transport Railway Company Limited was incorporated by Act of the Canadian Parliament in 1882, with the promise of a Government subsidy, and despite financial and political problems of no mean order the capital was eventually secured with the help of Baring Brothers in 1889. A contract was then let to John G. Meiggs, a brother of the fabulous American railway builder in Chile and Peru, Henry Meiggs. A good deal of work was done, the roadbed was completed and the docks and buildings at the Baie Verte end were almost finished; but Meiggs got into serious difficulties in the Argentine and although twelve miles of railway had been laid and much of the material was ready, work was suspended in August 1891 and never resumed.[16]

Mr Charles Hadfield has just drawn my attention to an illustrated article in *The Engineer* 11 Oct 1895 describing an amphibious passenger boat *Svanen* designed to travel overland, self-propelled, on a special railway between two lakes Fure So and Farum So near Copenhagen. This actually entered service on 15 June 1895. The inventor was a Swede, L.C.J. Magrell. The vessel was a steam launch 46 feet long and 9 feet six inches wide, driven by a propeller in the water. By engaging a clutch the drive could be diverted to one of the two pairs of railway wheels with which it was fitted.

CHAPTER VII

INCLINES CONNECTED WITH CANALS, NOT CARRYING BOATS

There have been a good many inclines leading up or down from canals or connecting two lines of canal, on which boats were not actually carried. It would be out of the question to mention all such inclines, but some may be singled out as being of unusual interest.

The earliest use of such an incline in conjunction with a canal in England seems to have been at the Carclaze tin mine near St. Austell.[1] At some date in the first part of the eighteenth century, a Mr. Parnall made a canal about half-a-mile long to bring the tin stuff out of the mine, and this is said to have terminated in a slide, down which the contents of the boats could be slid to load them into carts. The authorities on this incline are rather obscure — the author of the article on Canals in Rees' *Cyclopaedia* dated the canal about 1770. There seems little reason to doubt that after some years a roof fall imprisoned the boats and terminated the use of the canal, though the boats were re-discovered during a re-working about 1850.

Whether or not Parnall's Canal had an incline, the next canal to be mentioned, also in Cornwall, had two. This was the ill-fated St. Columb Canal, projected by John Edyvean and built under an Act of Parliament of 1773.[2] This canal was intended to carry similar cargoes to those carried later on the Bude Canal — sea sand for fertiliser and so on — and was to be built from Trenance Point near Mawgan Porth inland, circling round to the coast again at Lusty Glaze south of St. Columb Porth. Construction started at both seaside ends, and according to Rees' *Cyclopaedia* at one end at least the cliff was 'hewn down, into a steep inclined plane, that was covered with planks.' The canal ran to the top of the incline, and there the rectangular boats were tipped by a rope attached to a horse whim and the contents (usually stone) shot down the cliff; the horse whim was also used to haul up boxes of sea sand and coals for loading onto the canal boats. This description is said to refer to the Lusty Glaze end, where the course of the canal and the slide down the cliff can still be seen. An eye witness account also mentions the Trenance Point incline so that both must have been completed. The size of the boats is not known, though as the canal was quite narrow no doubt they were tub boats broadly similar to those later used on the Bude Canal.

The canal was not a success, though part of it seems to have been used for two or three years. John Edyvean appears to have been ruined by the project: there is a pathetic description of the old blind man conducting a visiting party among the canal works.[3] The idea of carrying sea sand inland for fertilizer was proved to be sound by the Bude Canal.

About 1774, a 'long and wide inclined plane' at an incline of about 45° was made from the quarries of Thomas Thornhill at Lillons Wood, Ealand, Yorkshire down to the Calder River;[4] this was paved with large flat stones, and self acting, a descending sledge loaded with stones drawing up an empty sledge by means of a rope over a wheel and axle. Rees said that these quarries were disused before 1783.

During 1794 the Coalbrookdale Company started to replace the vertical shafts for lowering goods at the end of the Brierly Hill branch of the Old Shropshire Canal (which will be described later) by a self-acting incline, which appears to have been brought into action at the end of September 1794.[5] This was still in use in August 1796 when the Prince and Princess of Orange, who were living in England after being ejected from Holland by the French Revolutionary armies, toured the Coalbrookdale Works. About 1800, a tramroad from Brierly Hill to Horsehay replaced that section of the canal branch. Exactly how the self-acting incline worked is not known. According to a valuation of the Coalbrookdale Company's works in about December, 1793, the inclined plane was then valued at £197 2s. 4d.[6] At that time fifty-seven wagons had been made for it and there were forty-five unfinished ones. In March 1796, a notice from the firm mentioned that . . . 'many People have of late feloniously taken coals . . . from the Incline-Plane' and threatened to Prosecute them 'as the Law directs'. Presumably after 1800 the inclined plane remained in use but any transhipment to canal boat took place elsewhere, not at the head of the incline.

After the completion of the Coalport incline of the Shropshire Canal at the Hay in 1792, a short length of canal was constructed along the riverside parallel to the Severn, but at a little distance. No permanent direct connection was made between the canal and the river, (though a lock was in course of construction in 1792), no doubt because tub-boats such as were used on the canal were quite unsuited to river navigation.[7] Some other means of transferring traffic from the canal to the river had to be found, however, and on the Madeley Tithe Award map no less than eight little inclines are shown between the canal and the river. These railways were not for carrying tub-boats, but the traffic must have been heavy on them as they had double track sections in the middle to enable wagons to pass on their way up and down. They are described as being 'for the descent of coals into the boats of the Severn'.[8] Some at least seem to have been put in before 1794, as in that year the engineer of the River Weaver was sent to study 'railed roads and other works . . . for shipping goods into vessels on the River Severn'.[9] This might have been at Coalbrookdale, but as the Weaver Navigation Trustees were thinking of trans-shipment at Anderton, it would seem more likely that they had these Coalport inclines in mind. As navigation on the Severn in the Ironbridge area virtually ceased after the opening of the Severn Valley Railway in 1862, no doubt these inclines fell into disuse about that time.

The Weaver Navigation Trustees in Cheshire were always unusually enterprising, and following suggestions from salt interests at Middlewich in 1788 they considered making means of transhipment at Anderton, where the Trent and Mersey Canal comes close to the river and about fifty feet above it.[10] By 1793 they had made a cut there to a basin, and the use of hand carts was introduced; these were loaded from canal barges and then tipped from a stage into Weaver 'flats'. Later chutes were constructed for tipping white salt down the hillside. About the end of 1799 a tramway was provided for rock salt and merchandise — presumably an incline down the bank from the canal — and a second one in 1800. Traffic upwards in china clay for the Potteries also developed. After 1807, as a result of a deal with the Trent and Mersey Canal, most of the arrangements for trans-shipment at Anderton were removed; but the salt traffic continued, general traffic was again authorised in 1826 by an Act of Parliament, and in 1832 another tramway was provided for coal traffic. As this traffic apparently did not develop, the tramway was used for rock salt. The traffic at Anderton grew, and in 1865, Edward Leader Williams (1828-1910) the Weaver engineer, suggested 'tramways worked by steam power' at Anderton.[11] At the end of 1867 he was ordered to relay the old tramway and build separate sets of tracks for coal and salt. By 1870 the time was ripe for the installation of the Anderton boat lift. The preamble of the Act for that lift mentions 'steam hoists, inclined planes and other machinery' at Anderton.

In 1803, an Act was obtained for the Tavistock Canal, which has already been mentioned in connection with the Millhill incline which carried boats. At the Morwellham end of the canal, however, where trans-shipment of goods to sea going vessels took place, there was an incline which was 720 feet long and $240\frac{1}{2}$ feet in vertical height, with an inclination reaching one in six.[12] Von Oeynhausen and von Dechen wrote: 'the self-acting plane has two parts, one of which leads to the level of the river; the other ends 30ft. above this point.'[13] then, contradicting the description of the incline as self-acting, they go on: 'Above, at the end of the canal, there is a waterwheel by which the empty wagons are drawn upwards'. The iron wagons which ran on the incline had one set of wheels fifteen inches in diameter and one set eighteen inches in diameter, and were arranged for tipping. Although it is not quite clear, it appears that trains of wagons ran up and down the incline. The waterwheel was driven by waste water from the canal, and was four feet wide and twenty-eight feet in diameter. Two drums were fitted on which the chains which were used to raise and lower the wagons were wound. These were so arranged that descending wagons helped the waterwheel to raise the ascending wagons, and when the train reached the top there was an arrangement by which the waterwheel was automatically thrown out of gear so that it continued to turn, but did not engage with the drums. There was also a brake mechanism provided.

It appears that originally it had been intended to carry goods up and down the incline in boxes, which could then be loaded onto boats, but it is doubtful whether this part of the scheme was put into effect, as the German engineers do not mention boxes.[14] As the wagons tipped, the boxes were probably deemed to be unnecessary. The tracks were originally of tramroad type, with a gauge of forty-six inches, but these were found to be unsatisfactory and were replaced by flat headed rails. The site of the pit which housed the waterwheel to drive the incline drums can still be discerned near Canal Cottage, but this is strictly private property. The sides of the terminus of the canal at Canal Cottage are reinforced, presumably to withstand the weight when transhipping the cargoes.

The canal was opened in 1817, the usual jollifications taking place on 24 June. Traffic on the canal varied with the activity in the mining industry; in 1859 the machinery of the plane was renewed at a cost of £300 to meet railway competition, but following the opening of the South Devon and Tavistock Railway on 24 June 1859, traffic fell off. In May 1873 an Act was passed to sell the canal to the Duke of Bedford. In 1883 the canal was supposed to be still open, but the incline was certainly disused in 1887.[15] Again, the engineer responsible was John Taylor. It has been stated that this incline carried boats, but this is plainly an error. Morwellham is now an industrial archaeology centre and part of the site of the incline has been cleared.

Another self-acting plane is mentioned by von Oeynhausen and von Dechen as running from a limestone quarry near Bath to the 'Avon Canal'.[16] This self-acting plane, of a total vertical height of 480-500 feet, consisted of a double cast-iron tramroad, and was 2,658 feet in length, divided into two divisions; the upper division, 1,658 feet long, was not of uniform slope, the lower portion sloped at about 5°. The gauge was three feet four inches and there were crossing switches at top and bottom; the rails rested on stone sleepers. There was a conical rope drum at the head of the incline, with a brake wheel on one side. The loaded traffic was of course down from the quarries, and the wagons carried up to seventy hundredweight of stone each. The German engineers noted that the rails were not heavy enough for the loads, but the owners were replacing broken rails by exactly similar ones, which seems shortsighted.[17]

There were also a number of temporary inclines, put in while flights of locks were being constructed.

In March 1797 the Peak Forest Canal, which was being cut in sections, an upper section from Bugsworth to Marple and a lower section from Dukinfield (junction with the Ashton Canal) to Marple, had to suspend construction for lack of money.[18] It was eventually decided to complete construction of the upper and lower lengths of canal and connect the two by a tramroad supplied by the Butterley Company, in which the engineer of the canal, Benjamin Outram, had an interest. This was a single track tramroad, and as a lower toll was charged if the limestone which formed the chief traffic was carried in iron boxes, presumably these boxes were winched out of boats at the top and into boats at the bottom. No less than fifty wagons were required for the incline, carrying two to two-and-a-half tons each, and the canal company required a minimum of 1,000 tons a day to be handled. Night working was introduced in December 1800 and in 1801 the tramway was doubled. Sir Richard Arkwright eventually advanced the money to build the line of locks, which were opened in October 1804, but surprisingly enough the Marple tramroad continued in use till February 1807.

The best known of these temporary inclines is the incline at Combe Hay on the Somersetshire Coal Canal. This canal was intended to carry coal from the Camerton and Radstock areas to the Kennet and Avon Canal near Limpley Stoke, and the line as surveyed involved a rise of approximately 120 feet at Combe Hay. Although the water supply for the canal was considered ample, in the interests of economy the proprietors originally intended to instal three caisson locks at Combe Hay. On the failure of the experimental lock (as explained later) the advice of Benjamin Outram was sought, and on 10 February 1800 he suggested the installation of an inclined plane.[19] He went further and suggested that the coal should be moved in wagons of forty hundredweight capacity from the collieries by tramway to the canal, where the wagon bodies would be lifted from the frames by crane and placed on special boats designed to carry twelve at a time. On arrival at Combe Hay, they would be transferred onto frames again, taken down the inclined plane, and again put onto boats for passage to the canal wharf at the destination, where he envisaged the wagon bodies being hoisted onto cart frames and taken direct to the consumer by road. One drawback of this scheme was that the tramways already existing would have to be relaid and strengthened, to carry the large capacity wagons. The canal engineer, William Bennet, advised against Outram's scheme as he favoured a continuous line of conveyance by water without any sort of transfer system, nor did he favour a suggestion that the wagon bodies should be formed into rafts for travelling along the canal. He also pointed out that a boat capable of carrying twelve forty hundredweight wagons would be too long to navigate the curves on the canal.

After taking the advice of John Sutcliffe, a former engineer to the canal, who strongly advised the use of common locks, in June 1800 it was reported:[20]

> . . . The Coal Canal Committee has at length determined on the manner of passing from the upper to the lower level; which is by means of which is called in the North a Whimzey or Jenny. It is the business of this machine to regulate the descent of the waggons carrying boxes of a ton of coals each on an inclined plane, which are linked to an endless chain passing round a cylindrical wheel at the upper and one of the same diameter at the lower end. The coals being put into wooden boxes of a ton each at the pits, are to be lowered by a crane into the boat, and from thence passed to the Whimzeys at Combhay, where three of them are again taken out by a crane and placed on a carriage

that stands on the inclined plane ready to receive them; on which, being attached to the chain, by its own gravity it descends 300 yards in five minutes, and at the same time brings up on the other side of the chain, the waggon and boxes that had gone down before, and which might, if necessary contain a fourth of the quantity carried down. Thus between 200 and 300 tons per day may be transferred, and, should the trade increase, another apparatus of the same kind be erected at no great expense. The deep cutting at the bottom of the plane will be saved by three locks.

The opening of this inclined plane was delayed by lack of finance but was eventually announced in November 1801.[21] The Kennet and Avon Canal Committee were not impressed, describing it in their Report on 10 May 1802 as 'extremely inconvenient and difficult to pass'. The Somersetshire Coal Canal committee evidently concurred, as they abandoned the idea of installing a second inclined plane on their Radstock arm, and applied to Parliament for powers to raise more money for a line of locks on both lines of the canal (in the event, only the Combe Hay locks were built). By an Act of 1802, a 'lock fund' was set up jointly by the two canal companies, and the lock fund bought the three locks at the bottom of the inclined plane, together with the inclined plane. The locks were finally opened on 5 April 1805 after a period of six weeks when the inclined plane had had to be shut down to complete the construction of the locks. So ended the Combe Hay inclined plane, which had been a sad disappointment. It even produced a lawsuit, when the refusal of traders to pay an additional toll for its use was upheld by the Court, in June 1806.

While the Devizes flight of locks on the Kennet and Avon Canal was being built, a double track iron railway on wooden sleepers was built about the end of 1802 from Foxhanger to Devizes — this was apparently not well carried out and the Canal Company expostulated with the contractors in December 1803. The flight of locks was completed in December 1810 and presumably the railway was then abandoned.[22]

A temporary line of rails is said to have existed about 1785 to connect the upper and lower levels of the Monkland Canal before the construction of the Blackhill locks, but very little is known about this.

CHAPTER VIII
COMPARTMENT LIFTS

There have been a number of schemes in connection with canals which have involved placing the cargo in boxes and transferring these boxes from one boat to another at changes of level. In practice none of these has lasted long, the labour and cost of transhipment having invariably been found uneconomic.

The first scheme of this sort actually put into practice was devised by Thomas Bridge of Tewkesbury, designed to circumvent the objections of the many local millowners to the canalisation of the Frome River from the Severn to Stroud in Gloucestershire.[1] Bridge had been employed in surveying the Frome for an abortive scheme of canalisation in 1755, and was well aware of the vehement objections of the millowners to the use of locks. He patented a plan for a 'machine navigation' in 1758. Cranes were to be mounted on walls twelve feet thick beside the mill weirs, worked either by hand windlass or by a bucket filled with water. As the bucket filled it drew up a box loaded with about one ton of cargo. When it reached its lowest level a trip mechanism allowed the water to flow out of the bucket and an empty box could then be lowered into the boat in place of the full one. As constructed the cranes seem to have been double-headed, capable of working either singly or in unison, so that a box could be raised from one boat and by turning the crane could then be reloaded into the boat on the other level. Special boats were built capable of carrying eight boxes.

In 1759 an Act of Parliament was obtained to enable this work to be carried out, and the commissioners of the undertaking let a contract to Bridge and three partners providing for payment on completion of the work. By April 1761 the contractors had made some progress and were given further time to carry out the works. These were completed for about five miles of the nine-and-a-half miles authorised, from Framilode almost to 'Mr. Hills Mill' near Nutshell Bridge, and then given up as the contractors ran out of money. It seems clear that the lower section of the machine navigation, as far as Churchend, was actually put into operation, when it soon became obvious that the scheme would never pay. It was far too clumsy, and there is some evidence that the boats (which carried up to ten tons) were too big for the river. In 1776 the remains of the works were still visible, but, of course, out of repair, and the cut was being used by certain millowners between one mill and another. One of the partners left hurriedly for foreign parts, Bridge pulled out early on, and the other two partners, John Kemmett and James Pynock, seem to have been in straitened circumstances for some years.

In 1765 James Brindley (1716-1772) installed a system calling for boats carrying twelve iron containers, each of which held eight hundredweight of coal, at the Manchester terminus of the Bridgewater Canal.[2] Canal boats from the Worsley mines entered a tunnel under a vertical shaft which led to the Castlefield, Manchester. The containers were then lifted up the shaft by a waterwheel-worked crane, emptied at street level, and lowered into the boat again. This system was replaced by a second waterwheel-driven hoist when the Grocers Warehouse was built at a date before 1789, but this hoist fell into disuse in 1800 when the Rochdale Canal was completed. A similar water-driven hoist operated between 1789 and 1800 at Shooters Bank Top about a half mile from Castlefield.[3]

Ducart's original proposals for the Coalisland Canal featured a tunnel which would double as a drainage and navigation level, into which containers holding ten hundredweight would be lowered from the colliery down a shaft thirty feet in diameter and 130 feet deep, by means of a capstan. The plans were revised, however, and the inclined planes already referred to were substituted.[4] As it is now known that Ducart visited Manchester about August 1768[5] no doubt he had seen the shaft on the Bridgewater Canal.

On the Donnington Wood Canal the rise of forty-two feet eight inches at Hugh's Bridge to the main line of the canal from the branch canal was originally surmounted by the branch running into a tunnel under two vertical shafts.[6] Goods in crates were raised or lowered by cranes at the top of the shaft, the cranes being interconnected so that the weight of descending goods (usually coal) would help to raise ascending goods (usually lime or limestone). This system was evidently found unsatisfactory as at some time, probably in the 1790s and certainly before 1797, the incline already described was substituted.

A similar scheme was put into effect in the early 1790s at Brierly Hill above Coalbrookdale, where the short lived canal branch from the Shropshire Canal reached the edge of the Severn Valley.[7] In this case the lower connection was provided by a railway from the Severn and the Coalbrookdale Works, which was carried into a tunnel under the hillside. At the canal basin, the boats carrying containers were placed in a dock and unloaded by cranes, and the containers raised and lowered down shafts to the railway below. The shafts were ten feet in diameter and 120 feet deep, and as at Hugh's Bridge counterbalancing was used.[8] However, these shafts did not last long; in 1794 work was put in hand to construct an incline to connect with the railway, which seems to have been put into use about 26 September 1794. The shafts were quite heavily used as it appears from the Coalbrookdale Company's account book that from 2 September 1793 to 10 October 1793, 1,801 tons of coal were lowered.[8]

According to Telford the boats carried four compartments, and he stated that the shafts employed a steam engine[9] (whereas the later incline did not) but other sources do not mention an engine.

The obvious disadvantages of transhipment and of the use of compartments have not encouraged the subsequent use of cranes and shafts to serve canals, and there does not appear to be much prospect of the system being revived in the future.

PART III

CHAPTER IX

CANAL LIFTS BEFORE 1820

The idea of lifting a canal boat vertically from one level of a canal to another, without the necessity of using up a lockful of water, seems to have been put into practice almost simultaneously in Germany and in England at the end of the eighteenth century; it seems unlikely that the German apparatus was known to contemporary English canal engineers.

In 1934, attention was drawn to the small boat lift which had been constructed in 1788-9 to connect the two levels of the Churprinz Canal[1] which ran for 5.3 kilometres on the left bank of the Freiberger Mulde River to carry ore from the Churprinz-Friedrich-August[2] Adit to the smelting works at Halsbrucke. The boats used carried 2.5 tonnes and were towed by two men, a third man on the boat steering with a pole. Just below the lift the canal crossed the Freiberger Mulde on the level and entered the 'Lifthouse' through a lower portal. This lifthouse was built of freestone, 5.5 metres wide and seventeen metres long, and the boats were lifted by manpower into the upper level by a five-fold tackle.

Although the arrangements were not altogether satisfactory, being liable to be disrupted by high water or bad weather, the lift continued in use till 1868. In 1934 its remains were still to be seen.

During the last decade of the eighteenth century the great period of canal building in England produced a number of schemes for canal lifts, primarily to enable canals to penetrate regions where water was not likely to be available in sufficient quantities for conventional locks. A number of highly ingenious designs for lifts were both patented and constructed, though unlike the Churprinz Canal lift they either proved to be unable to stand up to day to day use, or did not come into service on account of the canal proving to be abortive.

Of these early lifts, the one which perhaps came nearest to success was the 'hydrostatick' lift devised and patented by Robert Weldon, an enginer of Lichfield, in 1792.[3] According to the patent specification,

the machine consists of a trunk or cassoon made of copper, iron, wood or other materials, and of dimensions equal to the reception of vessels or other large bodies and weights. At each end thereof is a doorway, which the vessel, etc., are to be floated through, into or out of the trunk, and being received therein, and the door then shut with a given quantity of water to float the vessel etc. and counterpoize the machine, it may then be easily raised or lowered at pleasure by means of racks and pinions or chains and pullies (as shall be found most convenient), from one level to another, and the vessel etc., be delivered accordingly.

The cassoon moved in a shaft similar to a lockpit with a wall at each end having apertures which corresponded with the doors at the end of the cassoon,and with gates over the apertures which were raised or lowered by ratchets similar to those used for opening and closing sluices in locks to-day. The patent specification also envisages the use of 'a pump, an air pump, and other apparatus, to be applied as occasion may require'. The air pump presumably would be used to ensure a supply of air to anyone on the boat inside the cassoon. The lockpit was kept full of water normally, enabling the cassoon to move up and down relatively easily.

In 1794 Weldon constructed a demonstration model of his invention, presumably on a scale suitable for Shropshire Canal tub-boats, 'on the side of the Shropshire Canal, between Coalbrookdale and Donnington Wood, near the Oaken Gates, where the turnpike road from London to Holyhead crosses the said canal' according to a notice in the press, which also stated that the machine would be demonstrated every Monday, Wednesday and Saturday at 12 o'clock for six weeks after 26 September 1794.[4]

Exactly where this demonstration took place is not quite clear, as in 1794 the London-Holyhead road did not follow the route through Oakengates that it has followed since Telford reconstructed it between 1815 and 1830. The canal went underneath the old Watling Street and also under a road known as the Old Coach road which ran almost parallel to Watling Street, near Snedshill Furnaces, close to the point where the Ketley Canal met the Shropshire Canal. Mr. Howard Williams[5] points out that there seems to have been a difference in level of one foot six inches in between the two canals, which would provide a practical test for the hydrostatick lock.

The Kennet and Avon Canal Committee sent a deputation to view the demonstration, and had a small model made of the device.[6] In July 1795 the Kennet and Avon and Somersetshire Coal Canal Committees agreed to share the cost of erecting one of Weldon's locks, as an experiment, in the first place on the line of the Somersetshire Coal Canal near Radstock. The site of the experiment was later changed to Combe Hay, as the change of level there provided the opportunity to build two similar lifts should the first prove successful. The attraction was an estimated saving of £10,000 in costs over conventional locks, as well as a notable saving of water.

Weldon was made a sub-engineer to the Coal Canal and during 1796 and 1797 work continued on the caisson lock, the dimensions of which were: height from foundations to top sixty-one feet six inches; width twenty feet in the middle narrowing to eleven feet six inches at each end; length eighty-one feet. The dimensions of the wooden caisson were: eighty feet long, ten feet six inches wide and eleven feet six inches high. The chamber was stone built and was planned to have a lift of forty-six feet. A short approach tunnel led to its lower level, and difficulty was experienced in making the tunnel watertight. In November 1797 the work was so advanced that the caisson could be raised or lowered inside the lock chamber. On Friday 12 February 1798 a public trial was held and a great crowd assembled to watch. Alas, when the lock was nearly filled with water part of the adjusting apparatus gave way and let the caisson down at one end, when the pressure of water inside broke off the wheels which kept it parallel to the line of the canal and helped it to run up and down the chamber without friction; so that the trial ended in disaster. Repairs were put in hand, but by the middle of May when they were completed, there was insufficient water for a trial. At last, on Monday 4 June, the trial was resumed before a large crowd, and the machine worked perfectly, passing a boat from top to bottom, out of the chamber through the tunnel, and then back to the upper level. Weldon claimed that 1,500 tons of goods could be passed through the lift in twelve hours, with one man to work the machinery, assisted by the boatman.

The canal committee, however, deferred a decision on adopting the device till more trials had taken place, as during the trial, 'the working was retarded by a few obstructions altogether casual and which, in future may be entirely obviated'. There is a report (not apparently contemporary) that on one occasion the caisson stuck under water when some of the committee were in it, and by the time they were rescued all were at the point of suffocation.

Work went on to perfect the lift all through the winter and a further trial was held on Friday 5 April 1799 which was successful, and on 17 April the Prince of Wales himself attended a demonstration, when a boat was passed through the tunnel and raised to the upper levels, in less than two minutes. Then, after the boat had been taken out, the caisson was raised and lowered several times as a demonstration. It was again demonstrated on 27 April for over four hours; over sixty people including some ladies, made the journey, the average time being six-and-a-half minutes.

But in May, water seeping behind caused the stonework of the chamber to bulge and the Committee shortly afterwards decided to suspend work on the series of lifts until the inclined plane which has already been mentioned had been tried. The cost of the work had been £4,582 to date and the Canal Company was in serious financial trouble. Benjamin Outram was asked to report and he felt that to complete the series of lifts would cost at least another £16,000. This excluded the maintenance costs of the lift, which he thought would be heavy.

In view of this report, even though Outram blamed the masonry of the lift chamber rather than the nature of the apparatus for the failure, the Somersetshire Coal Canal Committee abandoned the attempt to use Weldon's lifts. Weldon himself seems to have remained in the neighbourhood; he died at Clifton in 1805.

Dr. Hugh Torrens has recently shown by analysis of the geology of the area that the immediate cause of the trouble with the chamber was the nature of the Lower Fuller's Earth Clay in which the chamber was excavated.[7] These clays have a varying ability to change volume by absorbing water; in wet periods the clay would exert heavy pressure on the walls of the chamber and cause them to bulge. Apparently similar trouble was experienced for precisely the same reason in the Sapperton tunnel of the Thames and Severn Canal.

The exact site of the caisson lock (or locks, as it appears that a second lockpit may have been commenced) is still not quite clear, but Dr. Torrens shows that the most likely site is to the south east of Caisson House at Combe Hay, where a guide book — admittedly written many years later — stated that 'the lower end of the chamber is marked by a chestnut tree'. There is only one chestnut tree in Caisson field, planted on an artificial looking mound. Perhaps investigation one day will show whether this suggested site is correct.

One might think that such an alarming device as the 'hydrostatick lock' would be forgotten, but a well reasoned report[8] in 1965 to the International Congress of Navigation at Stockholm drew attention to the theoretical advantages of the 'lift with immersed trough' on similar lines which had been devised by a German engineer named Rothmund and which had progressed to the stage of constructing models. The authors of the report strongly recommend that the scheme of Herr Rothmund should be investigated, as they felt that modern technical developments made it a practical proposition, and it had in their view great theoretical virtues. Whether the scheme will be followed up remains to be seen, but those who suffer from claustrophobia are unlikely to favour it.

Another design of lift, using only one chamber, was patented in 1794 by Edward Rowland and Exuperius Pickering, both of Ruabon in Denbighshire.[9] The Ellesmere Canal Company had obtained an Act in 1793 which included among other things power to construct a canal from Chirk to Pont Cysyllte, and thence in one direction to Llangollen and in the other to Chester via Ruabon. Edward Rowland was a shareholder in the canal and Exuperius Pickering a land and colliery owner in Ruabon.[10] The two men approached the Ellesmere Canal and offered to build a lift as an experiment, on the understanding that the canal would pay for it if it proved successful. The lift was to be capable of taking ordinary narrow boats as used on the Ellesmere Canal.

Their patent[11] provided for a well to be sunk on the site of the lift, of the same depth as the difference in height between the two canal levels, and this was to be filled with water. In it was to be placed a float, or diving chest, which 'may be made in manner and form of a boat, but closed at top and that so exactly no water shall be admitted, tho' sunk to the bottom of the well'. If the lift was to accommodate boats of twenty-eight ton burden, the float must contain 1,800 cubic feet vacuity, which would need a pressure of fifty tons in order to immerse it in water. On the diving chest were to be erected pillars of wood and iron high enough to reach the upper level when the diving chest was just immersed in the well, and on top of the pillars was to be a cradle, in the form of a boat, just large enough to admit a commercial boat inside it, and having a gate at each end. The inventors considered that the combined weight of the pillars, the cradle and the water in the cradle should be fifty tons, and thus balanced, the boat coming into the cradle would simply displace the equivalent weight of water (as Archimedes pointed out). The gates on the end of the cradle and of the canal levels being carefully fitted and water tight, on a boat being required to be passed, the cradle would be pressed up against the requisite canal gate, and the sets of gates raised so that the boat could pass. Once in the cradle and the gates lowered, the boat and cradle would be sufficiently easily balanced to be raised or lowered by a rack and pinion or other device. On arrival at the other level, it would be pressed up against the gate of the canal level and the gates opened to let the boat out. Rollers would be fitted on the sides of the lift shaft to facilitate the movement of the cradle.

This is a perfectly feasible scheme and uses only a very little water if leaks are prevented; it will be seen that later in the nineteenth century a similar plan was adopted in Germany with success. Presumably Telford, the resident engineer to the canal company, regarded it as possible, as the committee minuted on 4 December 1794 that he should point out as soon as possible, 'a place between Cysyltee and Chester' for the erection of the lift: 'Mr. Rowlands to bear the whole expence of trying the experiment and if it answers will expect to be paid as shall be agreed upon at the meeting . . . prior to his commencing the erection of his machine'.

In May 1796 it was announced in the press that the lift had been constructed, that a successful trial had been made, and that the proprietors would, for the inspection of engineers, have it working every Monday morning and Thursday evening. It was, according to Chapman, on a fall of twelve feet and could take the standard narrow boat seventy feet by seven feet.[11]

What happened then is not known, but it was not until June 1800 that Messrs. Rowland & Pickering applied to the canal committee for 'compensation for the expence of erecting their patent machine upon the canal . . .' and the committee decided to consult 'Professional men' as to whether 'the Machine has been constructed in principle materials and execution so as to be likely to answer the purpose intended in its present situation'. Mr. Jessop and Mr. Rennie had examined the machine and the committee asked them for their opinion in writing, which they gave on 4 August. Unfortunately no-one now knows what Jessop and Rennie actually reported; it must have been unfavourable but not damning, as the committee, taking into account that the device had cost the patentees £800 of which £400 could be recovered from re-use of materials, etc., decided to pay them £200 towards their loss, on 26 November 1800.[12] No more was heard of the invention, and it leaves open the intriguing question of where this quite large device was erected. Why it failed is another question, but it seems likely that contemporary materials and techniques were not equal to making the device strong enough to stand the strain of day to day operation.

Where, then, was it built?[13] The late L.T.C. Rolt considered that it was probably at Frankton Junction, where boats would be available and the fall through the locks is of the order of forty feet, giving good reason for the erection of a water-saving lift. The chief argument against this is geographical; Frankton is not really between Cysyllte and Chester when one remembers that the Ellesmere Canal Company had powers to build a line more or less direct, through Ruabon, nor does it readily fit the description 'near Ruabon' in the newspaper advertisement referred to. A second site suggested is in the Cefn and Acrefair area, in the direction which the direct canal line to Chester via Ruabon would have taken, where a lift economical in water would certainly have been useful to overcome the proposed rise of seventy-six feet near Plas Kynaston. It also appears that Rowland's brother was an ironmaster with landed property near Acrefair. If the lift was constructed in this area there are reasons for placing it at Cefn-Mawr near the bottom of the rise and within the area now occupied by the Monsanto Chemical works. Another possibility is that it was on the Ffrwd feeder branch, which was cut but probably never used, on the north side of Ruabon.

The arguments do in fact appear to be inconclusive and one can only hope that someone will eventually stumble across the remains of the lift, or some contemporary letter or entry in a diary will be found recording a visit to the lift. In a way it is surprising that no such literary reference has yet come to light.

In 1801 *citoyens* Bossu and Solages presented to the Institut in Paris a scheme for a lift on a similar plan to that of Rowland and Pickering, employing a float under a moveable caisson in which the boats were carried afloat. This plan was reported on by M. Charles Bossut, a well known mathematician. Not very much is known of the details of this device, but three such lifts were intended to be erected on the Creusot Canal already referred to. One lift was actually installed and tested at the end of the Creusot basin; at first it was not altogether successful, but after means of preventing leakage were worked out it proved satisfactory, and far more successful than the inclined plane tried on the same canal.[14]

As already related, the engineer responsible for the project, M. Gauthey, died in 1807 and the entire scheme for the canal was laid aside. It seems doubtful whether in everyday service the lift would have proved serviceable. The three lifts were designed to fall 8.45 metres, 5.36 metres and 4.55 metres respectively, but which was erected and tested is not known.[15]

The next experimental lift to be considered is that invented by John Woodhouse, an engineer successively on the Grand Junction Canal and the Worcester and Birmingham Canal. He obtained patents in 1806 and 1810[16] for 'conveying boats, barges or other vessels from one level of a canal to another without locks,' among other matters connected with canals. His original idea was to divide the upper and lower levels of a canal, the space between them (slightly longer than the boat to be raised or lowered) being divided longitudinally by a wall rising above the higher level sufficiently to allow the machinery to be erected on it. There were to be two containers in which the boats were to float, one on each side of the wall, and a number of wheels on top of the wall over which chains were to be passed to suspend the containers.

Woodhouse later modified his ideas and in his second patent he provided for only one container, to be balanced by counterweights on the other side of the wall, which he described as the 'lever wall', and in this form a lift was experimentally built on the site of the top lock of the Tardebigge flight on the Worcester and Birmingham Canal. The canal company agreed to pay for excavation and masonry if Woodhouse erected the machinery at his own expense. Edward Smith 'notary public accountant and canal agent' wrote an account of the lift as built.[17] The container, seventy-two feet long by eight feet wide by three feet six inches deep, made of three inch planking, and large enough to take a narrow boat, was suspended by eight rods and chains running over as many cast-iron pullies, balanced on the other side of the wall by an equal number of square frames laden with brickwork. Under the container and the counterweight were hung lengths of chain to render the counterbalancing more exact. There were 'paddles' at each end of the container, and also at each end of the canal, the space between which was filled with water when required by a valve. The pair of paddles at the requisite end of the container were then lifted to allow a boat to go in or out.

Edward Smith described a trip through the lift which he had taken. He said that the boat was raised twelve feet to the upper level 'without noise or jarring' by wheels and pinions on the other side of the wall, worked by two men. The trough was guided by small wheels running against corner posts. Two of the eight wheels at the top were toothed, and linked by pinions to handwheels for raising and lowering.

The lift was built during 1808 and was ready on 24 June 1808[18] though it could not be used for some time because the Tardebigge tunnel was not finished till the end of 1810. On 26 February 1810 it was tested, and passed a boat in two-and-a-half minutes. As 1810 wore on, apparently the canal committee became more and more doubtful about the lift and on 1 January 1811 decided to use locks at Tardebigge instead. Some of the shareholders in the canal favoured the lift, and called in Jessop, who reported in its favour mainly because he thought the cost of pumping water up to the summit level would be so high.

Between 25 February and 16 March 1811 there was a series of trials, on one of which the lift passed one hundred and ten boats in twelve hours. Rennie was then called in and reported, no doubt quite correctly, that the lift worked satisfactorily but was too delicate and would require constant expenditure on maintenance. He therefore recommended that it should not be adopted. The fact that it needed two men to work it was, of course, also a drawback, cheap as manual labour was in those days.

It appears that it was not replaced by a lock till 1815; the difficulty over water supply having been partly solved by the making of two reservoirs on the top level. The canal was not opened throughout till December 1815, so it is doubtful whether the lift actually saw much practical service. On two counts it appears to have been unique among canal lifts: it was roofed over; and on one occasion it was struck by lightning. It too was a primitive version of a type of lift which has been built in the twentieth century.

The first experimental lift to be constructed in which two counterbalancing caissons for boats were employed to reduce the amount of effort or water used in a movement of a boat was patented by James Fussell (1748-1832) of Wells in Somerset in 1798[19] and fitted up on the abortive Dorset and Somerset Canal. Only the Nettlebridge branch of this canal was started, but as not even this was completed, Fussell's invention hardly got a fair trial. Most unfortunately the records of the canal company were destroyed by enemy action during the 1939-45 War, but a good deal can still be found out about the 'balance lock'.[20]

James Fussell was an edge tool maker, a member of a family which was celebrated for its ironworks at Mells during the late eighteenth and early nineteenth centuries and until recently for its excellent brewery at Rode. He was also one of the leading directors of the Dorset and Somerset Canal.

His patent describes a lock pit which he thought might be as much as forty to fifty feet deep, open at the end on the lower level and with two side walls and an end wall to the top level. There was also to be a partition wall to divide the lockpit into two equal parts. Over the centre partition was fixed a shaft with wheels on it slightly wider than the partition, so that chains working over the wheels hung clear of the partition. The 'receptacles' were two open boxes, about six feet wide and two to three feet deep, made of wood, and water-tight. Under each receptacle was a strong oak framing to carry wheels corresponding to those on the shaft.[21] The receptacles and frames had wheels on the corners to run in the pits and keep the moving parts steady. The receptacles had chains hanging down (as in Woodhouse's lift) to assist in balancing them more perfectly. The chains to raise and lower the receptacle ran from the far side of one lockpit, under one receptacle, over one of the centre wheels, under the other receptacle, and thence to the far side of the other lockpit. To regulate the movement of the lift there was a tooth wheel on the centre shaft working into a pinion on a small shaft, which carried a flywheel and brake.

The ends of the receptacles were to be clipped to the ends of the canal and water admitted into the space. The 'hatches' at the clipped ends would then be drawn, and a boat floated in or out of the receptacles. Then the hatches would be replaced, and the water in the area between the top canal end and the receptacle would be drawn off into a tank under the receptacles, thus providing enough extra weight to cause the lift to work, movement being controlled by the flywheel and brake.

As the Dorset and Somerset Canal was expected to face problems of lack of water the committee evidently proposed from the first to use lifts, and after the failure of Weldon's scheme on the nearby Somersetshire Coal Canal, Fussell's scheme was adopted. The first complete lift, at Barrow Hill near Mells, was tried out on 6 September 1800, on a difference in level of twenty feet and was so successful that a public trial was made on 13 October to the general satisfaction. The boats used were of ten tons burden. The committee were so satisfied that they let contracts for five similar balance locks and when work ceased on the canal, due to lack of money, in 1803, as well as the trial lift there were four unfinished lockpits about half-a-mile to the east. It proved impossible to raise more money and no part of the canal was ever opened to traffic.

No other trial of Fussell's balance lock was ever made, but the general principles of his scheme were taken up by James Green a few years later, as will be seen. Judging from the comparative success of Green's lifts, Fussell's might well have worked satisfactorily had they been given the chance, especially since Fussell owned an ironworks and might be expected to have the moving parts adequately constructed. Of all the early schemes this and Green's seem to have been best adapted to the materials and techniques then available.

We move next to London, when the Regent's Canal Company was also faced with problems of water shortage on their line from Paddington basin of the Grand Junction Canal to the Thames at Limehouse. The directors were persuaded to try a 'hydro-pneumatic' lock devised by no less than Colonel Sir William Congreve (1772-1828) Bart., M.P., the inventor of the Congreve rockets which were used in the later battles of the Napoleonic wars and frightened the enemy's cavalry horses more than they damaged his equipment.

Colonel Congreve (as he then was) patented his lock in 1813.[22] The principle is not altogether easy to follow, being based on two counterbalancing inverted caissons working with their sides between the outer walls of the lockpits and lower inner walls. These caissons were airtight and trapped air under them, the air being able to pass from one lockpit to the other through a passage. Assuming one caisson was at the upper level of the canal and the other at the lower level, enough water was run onto the top of each caisson to equal the respective water levels in the canal, the gates from the canal opened and a boat floated into each lockpit above the caisson tops. By working a rack and pinion or an air pump the 'inertia' of the counterbalancing was, according to Congreve, to be overcome and the two caissons would move, one up and the other down, so that the respective boats were moved to the other level of the canal. Congreve claimed that as the caissons were to be supported by columns of air no water would be lost at all from the upper level of the canal but obviously the scheme depended for its success on the caissons being thoroughly airtight; even though the experimental lock was constructed by Henry Maudslay & Company, probably the most able firm in the capital, it proved impossible to ensure this. The patent scheme was put forward to the directors of the Regent's Canal in April 1814, and in December a contract was signed with Congreve, agreeing to pay him £250 for each lock constructed, and Maudslay's agreed to have a specimen lock ready by April 1815.[23] This proved impossible, the caissons could not be kept airtight and no doubt water leaked down the outside of them as well. The canal company meanwhile ran into a financial crisis. By March 1816 Maudslay had to admit that the lock would not pass a boat in the three minutes which Congreve had promised: however he said that it would pass a boat in four-and-a-half minutes worked by two men, or six minutes, if worked by one man. Shortly afterwards at a demonstration a boat was passed by one man in six minutes but his efforts at the air pump so exhausted him, that he was unable to make any further exertion for some time. Maudslay had already been paid £2,000 and now demanded the rest of his contract fee of £4,449, while claiming that the lift had cost him over £9,000. In August a further trial was arranged but when Maudslay wished to exclude the time taken up by opening and shutting the gates from the three minutes allowed for a movement the canal engineer refused to agree, and the meeting broke up. In June 1817 Maudslay was awarded £4,020 by an arbitrator and a year later, in July 1818, Congreve was paid his £250, and rather unkindly asked to assist in disposing of the machinery. It was sold by auction for £404. 17s. 11d. and no more was heard of Congreve's patent. The lift is described as having been at Hampstead Road so that it was presumably situated on or close to the site of the present Hampstead Road lock, the top lock on the canal. The difference in level is six feet eight-and-a-half inches and, presumably, the lift was made to accommodate the Regent's Canal wide boats, eighty feet long and fourteen feet six inches wide.

This was the last of the experimental lifts of the period around 1800; their failure is largely to be attributed to the deficiencies of the materials available at the time. Whether engineers learnt anything from their somewhat melancholy history or not, the subsequent history of the canal lift is one of ever increasing success.

CHAPTER X

THE GRAND WESTERN CANAL LIFTS

The canal lifts so far described had not proved viable, the fault being sometimes with the lift and sometimes with the canal itself; the only exception being the lift on the Churprinz Canal, though a lift worked by block and tackle was hardly capable of wide application. Subsequent canal lifts in general have proved workable, and many are still operating today.

James Green's plan for the seven lifts on the eastern section of the Grand Western Canal envisaged lifts capable of taking the Grand Western tub-boats, twenty-six feet long by six feet six inches wide and drawing two feet three inches of water when loaded.[1] In the six miles between Taunton and the foot of Trefusis lift, the canal rose fifty-five feet by lifts at Taunton (twenty-three feet six inches) Norton Fitzwarren (twelve feet six inches) and Allerford (nineteen feet); in the seven miles between Trefusis and Lowdwells, there were lifts at Trefusis (thirty-eight feet six inches) Nynehead (twenty-four feet) Winsbeer (eighteen feet) and Greenham (forty-two feet) as well as the incline at Wellisford between Winsbeer and Greenham lifts.

The plan of the lifts as originally designed was to have two chambers, like lock chambers, divided by a pier of masonry, with a wooden cradle in each chamber in which a boat could float. The cradles had lifting doors at each end. Arches were provided in the centre pier for access for inspection and repair of the lift. The cradles were suspended by chains from three large wheels fitted on a longitudinal shaft held by a frame on the centre pier. The centre wheel was fitted with a hand gear and brake so that the working of the lift could be regulated and if necessary the cradles worked by hand. Under each cradle were fitted counterbalancing chains which coiled up on the floor of the chamber as the cradle fell. A beam was provided on which the lower cradle rested when at the bottom of the lift; this beam could be adjusted so that the cradle would rest in the proper position in relation to the lower level of the canal. A forcing bar was provided at the top and bottom levels so that the cradles could be pressed against the upper and lower facings of the canal gates. The lift was set in motion by running extra water into the top cradle − in practice it was found that two inches of water provided about one ton additional weight, sufficient to work the lift.

On 21 June 1832 Green reported that construction of the Taunton

Allerford and Greenham lifts was well under way, in 1833 the other lifts were in a forward condition, and by January 1834 the Taunton lift was ready for trial. Then arose unforeseen difficulties. Originally Green had provided no means of cutting off the water in the lower lock chamber from the lower level of the canal, and the lower cradle came to rest slightly above the level of the lower canal. Presumably by hand-operating the lift it would be possible to force it down to the proper level but this would be very unsatisfactory. Dr. Anderson, who had originally suggested a similar lift in a paper attached to his *Agricultural Survey of the County of Aberdeen*, foreseeing this difficulty, had suggested having a stop lock at the exit from the lift, and draining off water from the lift bottom prior to each operation by means of pipes; this would provide the necessary extra weight to work the lift, but the water drained off would be lost to the canal, which would nullify one of the major advantages of the system, its great economy in water. By the time this defect in the lifts was discovered it was too late to modify four of the lifts in the most satisfactory way. Fortunately in May 1836 the canal committee commissioned a report from W.A. Provis which gives a clear account of the lifts as finished, showing that they varied considerably in construction.

In June 1836 Provis inspected the works, and found that the Taunton, Norton & Allerford lifts were broadly similar. In each case after the design deficiency had been discovered stop gates had been fitted at the lower end of the canal, and pipes fitted to draw off the surplus water; but apparently the pipes could not deal with the water quickly enough and pairs of locks were fitted at the lower end of the caisson. On a boat reaching the lower level, water was let into the lock from above till the level was high enough for the boat to be floated out of the cradle into the lock: the lock was then emptied in the usual way into the lower pound so that the boat sank to the level of the lower pound.

The Trefusis, Nynehead and Winsbeer lifts not having reached an advanced stage before the error was discovered, had vertical gates fitted at the lower level which could be clipped to the cradles' gates and both lifted simultaneously. This shortened the locks at the lower end and enabled water to be saved. The Greenham lift eliminated the lock by having pipes fitted to draw off the surplus water; this wasted the water completely from the point of view of the canal, but this was not as important as it might have been since the Lowdwells stop lock, passing four boats at a time, drew three feet of water from the summit level every time it worked.

Provis mentioned various accidents which had happened to the lifts, which do not seem unduly serious considering that an entirely novel technique was being tried; at the Taunton lift on one occasion, due to carelessness, water was drawn from the lower cradle when the upper one was loaded, so that the upper cradle fell too rapidly and was broken; at the Norton lift, the main shaft had broken and one cradle damaged in consequence; at Allerford, the pinion in the centre wheel had broken. These lifts had been working for more than two years in June 1836. Apparently

Trefusis, Nynehead and Allerford lifts had been working since Summer 1835: the main shaft had broken early in 1836 at Trefusis; at Nynehead, a few cogs of one pinion broke when the lift first was set to work; at Winsbeer, one bevel wheel in connection with the brake mechanism had broken; at Greenham, there had been some settlement of the caisson chambers at first. Provis' main criticism was that except at Trefusis only a single brake was fitted, which he considered insufficient.

According to James Green[2], a boat could be passed up and one down, a lift of forty-six feet, in three minutes: but Provis timed a loaded boat from entering the lock at the lower level to floating into the upper pond of the canal at eight-and-a-half minutes. Possibly one is not comparing like with like, but Green does seem optimistic.

The basic reason for installing the lifts and incline on the canal was to economise in water. The use of thirty locks which had been suggested earlier by Benjamin Bevan would have necessitated two reservoirs at the summit level, which Green's plans dispensed with. Indeed, Green claimed that theoretically if trade were all downward, water would be raised to the summit level, but this seems a bit too good to be true in practice. Green also claimed a great saving in time, and with the deeper lifts there may well have been a considerable saving when they were working properly.

The opening of the Bristol and Exeter Railway to Tiverton in 1848 led to a crisis in the canal's affairs, and after a rate war which ended in the canal charging no toll for coal to Tiverton, on the 20 October 1853 the canal was leased to the railway, and traffic on the section east of Lowdwells became negligible. It appears that a few boats carrying stone passed occasionally, so that the lifts were worked from time to time; but the machinery deteriorated. Finally by authority of an Act of Parliament[3], the canal was sold to the Bristol and Exeter Railway on 13 April 1865, and the Taunton-Lowdwells section closed in 1867 and dismantled. This was a sad end to a brave experiment.

CHAPTER XI

HYDRAULIC LIFTS

Edwin Clark (1814-1894)[1], a somewhat enigmatic figure, was the inspiration behind the group of successful lifts now to be described. Indeed, it is hardly too much to say that the canal lift owes its present standing as a sophisticated practical mechanism to his original design.

In 1846, Edwin Clark had met Robert Stephenson, who was impressed by his grasp of mathematics and appointed him superintending engineer to the Britannia tubular bridge. His interests came to lie in electrical and hydraulic engineering, and in 1857 he became the engineer to the Thames Graving Dock Limited, which proposed to construct a graving dock in which the ships to be repaired were lifted from the water by hydraulic presses.

As has already been mentioned the trustees of the Weaver Navigation had pursued a policy of improvement for many years, and the growth of the local salt and chemical industries caused great additional traffic. The trustees decided to make a physical connection with the Trent and Mersey Canal at Anderton to divert traffic from the Bridgewater Canal, which they feared might fall into the hands of a railway company.[2] They obtained from Edward Leader Williams, their engineer, proposals for an hydraulic lift to transfer barges between the canal and the river navigation, and went to Parliament for powers to borrow money to carry out this lift, among other improvements. The Act passed in 1872[3] and work was started on the lift to Edwin Clark's design, Emmerson Murgatroyd and Company Limited being the contractors. Unfortunately, Leader Williams then left the Weaver Trustees' service to be manager and engineer of the Bridgewater Canal; later he was engineer to the Manchester Ship Canal. His successor, J. Watt Sandeman, modified the design to strengthen the foundations during construction, but the lift was duly finished and opened to traffic on 26 July 1875.

The difference of levels at the point chosen was fifty feet four inches, and the system adopted was of two counterbalancing troughs each supported on a central hydraulic ram.[4] The cylinders in which these rams worked had to be sunk seventy feet below the surface. The troughs were seventy-five feet long and fifteen feet six inches wide, so that they would each hold two narrow boats, side by side, when desired. Barges up to one hundred tons could be accommodated.

The aqueduct to the top level had two channels, each closed at the lift end by counterbalanced lifting gates, the troughs having similar lifting gates; the junction between the aqueduct and the trough was kept watertight by india-rubber on bevelled surfaces. Power for the hydraulic presses was provided by an accumulator worked by a small steam engine.

The system of working was as follows (assuming one trough to be at the top and the other at the bottom): the operator opened a valve on a five inch pipe connecting the two rams, and the upper trough descended, while the lower trough rose to within four feet six inches of the upper level. The valve was then closed and the water in the descending press allowed to run to waste, so that the trough descended into the water. Meanwhile a connection from the accumulator to the ascending trough press was opened, and the ascending trough was forced up to within six inches below the top of the lift. This was done to allow for running in extra water, so that the trough would be ready to be forced down later.

The india rubber and bevelled joint at the top was squeezed by the ascending trough to form a watertight joint; a valve was opened to fill the space between the gates, and then the aqueduct and trough gates were lifted, and water flowed in to equalize the levels. Any extra water in the lower trough could be drawn off by syphons.

The lift could pass two narrow boats each way in eight minutes; to pass eight boats each way took an hour.[5] If one trough was out of action the remaining trough could be lifted by the accumulator, but this took half an hour.

One criticism of the lift made at the time was that if any part of the mechanism of the Anderton lift gave way, the resulting accident would be very nasty, and comparison was made with the Blackhill incline which was claimed to be safer.[6] This theory was put to the test on 26 April 1882[7] when, just as the upriver gate of one trough had been raised preparatory to levelling up the water in the trough, the side of the press blew out and water from the upper level rushed into the descending trough, damaging a boat preparing to enter. Fortunately the water could not escape very rapidly from the press and the trough dropped fairly slowly onto a water cushion, but a workman engaged in greasing the rams had a very narrow escape. After consultation between L.B. Wells, who was at that time the Weaver engineer, Leader Williams and Emmerson Murgatroyd & Company, the press was made heavier and redesigned. During the six months' period of repair goods had to be hauled up and down the hillside on temporary rails.

The presence of chemical effluent in the water caused increasing trouble from 1884. The top ends of the rams became grooved or corded, and these grooves as much as eight feet long, were repaired by letting in bar copper on an increasing scale. By 1895, this grooving caused so much concern that experiments to find the cause were carried out by Brunner Mond & Company, which traced it to electrolytic action. By the use of condensed water in the rams their life was extended till 1904, but after the replacement

76

of the steam boilers by electric pumps in 1902, the general condition of the mechanism gave increasing cause for alarm, and, as will be explained later, the lift was radically reconstructed into its present form. The use of the lift was in the earlier years somewhat disappointing but gradually increased over the years, so that it proved well worth the expenditure on modernisation.

Borne up by the success of the Anderton lift the partnership of Latimer Clark (1822-1898), younger brother of Edwin and primarily an electrical engineer, John Standfield and Edwin Clark went on to provide designs for lifts on the continent. In conjunction with the well known French engineering works, S.A. des anciens établissements Cail,[8] they designed an hydraulic lift for the Neufossé Canal, which joins the channel ports of the Pas de Calais to the Canal de St. Quentin, which links Lille and the Paris area. At a place called les Fontinettes, a flight of five locks formed a great hindrance to traffic, and, following a competition in 1880, the General Council of Bridges and Roads, the controlling authority for French canals, decided to instal a lift on Clark's system. This was to be larger than the Anderton lift and to be capable of taking three hundred tonne barges, 38.60 metres long, five metres wide and drawing two metres. The difference between the two canal levels was 13.13 metres and the site was rather cramped owing to the presence of the Boulogne-St. Omer railway which ran below the aqueducts which led to the top of the lift. The system of operation at les Fontinettes was the same as that of the Anderton lift as originally built, with counterbalancing troughs. The rams were two metres in diameter and the presses were claimed to be more than double the dimensions of the largest presses previously existing. The original intention was to make the presses in cast iron, but while they were being designed, the accident at Anderton was reported. Various other materials were then tried, and finally the presses were made of steel with an interior envelope of copper 0.0025 metres thick. A trial section was tested in the presence of several engineers, including Edwin Clark, M. Gruson, chief engineer for Bridges and Roads for the Douai area, and M. Barbet, chief engineer of Messrs. Cail. These experiments and the need to establish firm foundations in poor soil (*terrain détestable*) delayed the opening of the lift till 20 April 1888, the official inauguration taking place on the 8 July 1888, in the presence of the Minister of Public Works. There were various changes from the Anderton design. The troughs were supported in the centre on masonry towers, the centre tower also supporting the operator's cabin.[9] M. Seyrig, the superintending civil engineer, suggested gates which would fall onto the floor of the troughs to permit boats of all heights to pass, but this would have required longer troughs, and finally the gates of the canal levels and the troughs were made to lift vertically, being clipped together at each end before being lifted. An accident is reported on one occasion when the upper trough was lowered owing to a leakage, leaving its gates behind.[10]

One important alteration from the system used at Anderton provided for the pit into which the troughs descended to be kept dry. This was proposed by Edwin Clark, and did away with the necessity for the troughs to be moved for the final short distance by the accumulator; but it was remarked that the existence of the water at the lower level of the Anderton lift had minimised the effects of the accident in 1882 by cushioning the trough in its fall. At les Fontinettes, a turbine was provided to work a pair of hydraulic engines with accumulators to assist when necessary. Hydraulic power was used to compensate for any leakages in the presses, keep the pits dry, lift the gates and turn capstans at the entrances to the troughs. A smaller turbine was also provided to blow out the india rubber seals between the troughs and the canal.[11] A British Royal Commission inspected the lift and reported that in 1905, it had passed 11,161 boats with a total tonnage of 1,703,000 tonnes. It was noted that on each movement about 15,000 cubic feet of water was used, and the time taken to pass a boat was about twenty minutes. The locks which the lift replaced were not removed, so that when the lift was out of service for repair, traffic was not interrupted.

Originally, the lift was intended to be worked by a 'surcharge' of forty-one tonnes of water passing from one press to the other, with a corresponding surcharge of forty-one tonnes into the upper (descending) trough.[12] In practice fifty tonnes was found to be necessary. However, by 1896, the system had been changed; the valves between the presses were partially closed, and the lift was worked by adding thirty centimetres of water, or 63.5 tonnes, to the upper trough.

Enquiries made in 1950[13] showed that the lift 'had been spared by the war' and was still in regular service on the original system, with modifications to ensure the water-tightness of the troughs; but a recent enlargement of the canal to take boats of 1,350 tonnes involved the replacement of the lift by a single deep lock,[14] the lift remaining as an industrial monument.

Almost simultaneously with the work at les Fontinettes, the construction was commenced in Belgium of the Canal du Centre, which was intended to join the Brussels-Charleroi Canal at Houdeng to the Mons-Condé Canal, providing an outlet for the coal of the Meuse basin to west Belgium and northern France.[15] The difference in level between the two ends of the Canal du Centre was 89.45 metres, and was surmounted in two sections, one of thirteen kilometres containing five locks with a total rise of 23.26 metres, and the other of eight kilometres with a total rise of 66.19 metres; in the latter section there were to be four lifts, three with a rise of 16.93 metres and the fourth, (the first to be constructed) with a rise of 15.40 metres. These lifts were designed for boats of three hundred to four hundred tonnes, and the troughs were forty-three metres long, 5.80 metres wide and 2.60 metres deep. The first of the four lifts was designed by M.P. Nolet, an engineer employed by Messrs Clark Standfield & Clark, at the works of the Société Cockerill, Seraing.[16] In the older publications it is always described as being at La Louvière, but modern guidebooks refer to it as being at Houdeng-Goegnies.[17]

This lift was essentially similar to the lift at les Fontinettes, but as much water was required to work the locks further along the canal, no effort was made to effect the maximum saving of water and the lift was generally worked by a surcharge of twenty-five centimetres of water – sixty-two tonnes – in the upper trough.[18] This has subsequently been increased to thirty centimetres – seventy-five tonnes.[17] Unlike the French lift, the construction was of lattice girders. The ram was two metres in diameter and 19.44 metres high. The lift was operated by the working of a central sluice-gate situated in the pipe between the two presses. The pits at the lower end of the lift were kept dry, as at les Fontinettes, and the machinery was worked by two turbines, arranged with horizontal axes on the Girard principle. Vernon Harcourt described the lift at La Louvière as 'a decided improvement on the Fontinettes lift'.[15]

The original lift was accorded the honour on 4 June 1888 of being opened by Royalty, no less than King Leopold II of the Belgians; but unfortunately the occasion did not pass off without incident, as one of the onlookers shouted 'Down with Coburg' and was thereupon arrested and thrown into prison at Mons.[19] For some reason there was considerable delay in erecting the remaining three lifts – it seems unlikely that this lack of enthusiasm for Royalty had anything to do with it. Although the first lift had only taken four years to instal, the other three were not opened to traffic till August 1917 when the Germans were occupying the area. They should have been ready in 1915, but the war delayed completion.[20] The civil engineering work of the later lifts was done by the S.A. de Construction de Hal, the mechanical part by the Société Cockerill. The vertically lifting gates of the trough were sealed to the canal gates by rubberised joints, a small hydraulic press being used to ensure a close fit. The gates were not fitted with counterweights as those at La Louvière had been. The control cabins were fitted at the top of the centre support, and a signalling device showing the precise position of the troughs at any time was provided. The two centre lifts at Houdeng-Goegnies and Bracqueginies share a hydraulic system worked by a sixty horse power turbine. The fourth lift is at Thieu. The lifts are concentrated on a stretch of canal 4.1 kilometres long, the two centre ones being only 0.24 kilometres apart.

The lifts of the Canal du Centre have proved successful and are linked with the incline at Ronquières as a tourist attraction by the Tourist Federation of Hainault.[17] On an average, they pass thirty boats a day, and the original one holds the record by passing in one day between 4 a.m. and 9 p.m., no less than seventy-two boats. They were the last lifts to be built under the auspices of Messrs. Clark Standfield & Clark, in spite of the Société Cockerill's energetic attempts to find further orders which included issuing a pamphlet on them by MM. Freson and Genard in French, English and German editions. Recently, it has been decided to replace the four lifts with a single lift of no less than 73.15 metres to be situated near Strepy, half way between the present lifts three and four. This lift is intended to be similar to the Scharnebeck lift and to be completed in 1985, but in 1978, no work on the lift had commenced, though some of the necessary earthworks on the new stretch of canal had been carried out.[21]

News of the success of the hydraulic system spread across the Atlantic and in addition to the abortive lifts of the Chignecto Ship-Railway, two lifts were installed on the Trent Canal in Ontario, Canada. These still operate, though it appears that commercial traffic (as distinct from pleasure traffic) has ceased. They were constructed betwen 1895 and 1907, one at Peterborough, with a rise of sixty-five feet and the other at Kirkfield, with a rise of fifty feet. The troughs of the lifts are 140 feet long and thirty-three feet wide, with a depth of eight feet and the clear headway is twenty-five feet.[22] The engineers responsible for their design were R.B. Rogers and Walter J. Francis and in general followed the previous designs closely, employing the principle of the hydraulic presses and 'dry pits' into which the troughs descend. The troughs are guided by three towers supporting them in the centre. One feature is that the 'breast wall' at Peterborough is pierced by a road tunnel fourteen feet wide and twenty-one feet high, forming a continuation of the main street of Peterborough. The wells in which the presses are situated are seventy-five feet deep.

The gates at the ends of the canal and the troughs were designed to be always lifted in pairs, and provided with galvanised air chambers to render them practically buoyant. Each gate is hinged at the bottom, and was originally operated by means of small hydraulic engines working pinions in racks on the sides of the walls. When open, the gates lie flat on the bottom leaving the full depth available for navigation. The gates and the chambers are kept watertight by rubber strips and the space between the pairs of gates is filled by inflatable rubber tubes. The only change which has been made in operation over the years, is that the gates and valves are now worked by electricity, not by hydraulic engines.

The rams are ninety inches in diameter and have a stroke of sixty-five feet at Peterborough and fifty feet at Kirkfield. They are built up of cast iron sections each five feet three inches long, and the presses are plain steel castings built up of sections of similar lengths. The lift is controlled by a gate valve in the middle of the pipe connecting the two presses. An hydraulic accumulator was fitted, obtaining its water supply from a pump worked by a fifteen inch horizontal 'Crocker' type turbine driven by water from the upper reach. There was an air compressor providing air for an air lift which kept the pits dry. The chief difference in construction between the Peterborough and Kirkfield lifts, is that the towers are of concrete at Peterborough and of steel at Kirkfield.

The contractors for the embankment and substructure of the Peterborough lift, were Messrs. Corry & Laverdure of Ottawa, who completed their work in 1902, and for the superstructure, the Dominion Bridge Company of Montreal, who completed their part of the contract in early July 1904.

No further lifts of the pattern originally designed by Edwin Clark have been erected.

CHAPTER XII

THE CANAL LIFT IN THE TWENTIETH CENTURY

The experience of the type of lifts introduced by Edwin Clark and involving the use of two caissons working as counterweights to each other has shown that, in general, traffic on canals is not sufficiently regular and equal in each direction, to render the working of two caissons in unison truly economic, in spite of the attractions of counterbalancing. Since 1899, lifts other than those on the Canal du Centre in Belgium and the Canadian Trent Canal have attained the object of balancing the laden caisson by other means, either by a series of counterweights (foreshadowed by Woodhouse's lift) or by floats (following the proposals of Rowland and Pickering or Bossu and Solages).

It has already been explained that the Anderton lift suffered from grooving of the rams as a result of chemical action, and that only the use of distilled water prolonged the life of the rams beyond the early 1890s. In the late 1890s and early 1900s, there were repeated signs that the existing plant was wearing out, in 1898/9, there was a series of breakdowns due to pressure pipes giving way: in 1902, the steam plant was replaced by electric pumps as already mentioned; but in 1904, further failures of the pressure pipes led the engineer of the Weaver Navigation, John A. Saner, to take up the condition of the lift with the trustees as a matter of urgency.[1] At that time, 138 lifts were made every week, and 191,866 tons of traffic passed every year so that closing the lift for repair and renewal of the existing plant could hardly be contemplated. There being no room for constructing a longitudinal cofferdam, to enable one side of the lift to be rebuilt at a time, Saner proposed to retain the aqueduct and troughs or caissons, but to suspend the caissons on wire ropes passing over pulleys on overhead gantries, with counterweights at the free ends of the ropes.

This scheme was adopted and put into effect with only three stoppages of traffic of approximately fourteen days each. First, over Easter 1906, an inverted arched floor of reinforced concrete was put into the dock, so that the caissons would fall into a dry pit, and the balanced weight be constant. The next step, was to fit river gates to the dock, which was done during Stoke-on-Trent wakes week, 1906.

The new foundations for the new columns, and the whole of the new overhead structure was put in with the lift at work, so that, at Easter 1908, everything was ready to disconnect the old ram on the No. 1 caisson, couple up the new pulleys, and render the new system workable for the No. 1 caisson. This only took a fortnight, and similar work to change over the No. 2 caisson was completed for the official opening on 29 July 1908. The two caissons now ran independently of each other, and the traffic could be handled by one caisson only if desired. All this work was carried out by direct labour.

The total weight to be suspended was 1,000 tons, each caisson weighing 250 tons (of which eighty tons was iron and the rest water) and the counterweights the same. Each counterweight is limited to seven tons; the pulleys are arranged at regular intervals with the actuating motors in the centre of each row. The electric motors were thirty brake horse power working 750 r.p.m., geared down so that the pulleys revolved much slower. One movement of a caisson takes about six minutes.

The reconstruction increased the capacity for traffic of the lift, and reduced its consumption of electricity by about a third. In 1913, the traffic transferred was a record, at 226,000 tons,[2] and the lift has worked perfectly successfully to this day, a remarkable memorial to the skill and energy of successive chief engineers of the Weaver Navigation, not to mention the business capacity of the trustees.

Since the 1939-45 war, commercial traffic through the Anderton lift has virtually disappeared, though it remains the only waterway access from the Northwich repair yard to the narrow-boat canal system. It is, however, used by an increasing number of pleasure craft, and as there is a statutory duty to maintain it, the British Waterways Board have recently carried out extensive repairs spread over two winters.[3] Fortunately, the demise of commercial traffic has enabled the lift to be closed during the winter months for repair. Much of the steelwork was found to be corroded, and was either replaced or grit-blasted and prime painted. The main drive gear has also been steam cleaned, prime painted and overhauled. The work was done under the supervision of Husband & Company as consulting engineers, with the Butterley Engineering Company Limited as main contractors.

In April 1981, while a private narrow boat was being lowered in the west caisson, a leak developed in the gate seal and, released from the weight of water in the caisson, the counterweights took over and raised the caisson to the top; the passengers in the boat got out safely but a certain amount of structural damage was done which took seven months to repair.[4] As Cheshire County Council are planning to build a museum complex centred on industrial history next to the lift, pleasure craft is likely to be drawn to the lift in increasing quantities.

However, there is no doubt that the country which has developed the lift most in the present century, using more than one system, is Germany. Firstly, there is at Niederfinow a lift similar to the rebuilt Anderton lift. The historical background of this can be traced to 1746, when Frederick the Great of Prussia opened the Finow Canal, which linked Berlin and Stettin (now Szczecin) by joining the Havel and Oder Rivers. This canal had eighteen locks and took boats of 250 tons, In 1914, the Finow Canal was superseded by the Hohenzollern Canal from Spandau on the Havel to Hohensaaten on the Western Oder; this could take vessels of 600 tons, falling 116 feet to the Western Oder by four locks at Niederfinow. Negotiating this flight of locks took about two hours, and the installation of a second flight of locks was considered. Instead, it was decided in 1926 to instal a lift, which would cater for one boat of 1,000 tons or four boats of 225 tons, and greatly reduce the time and trouble of locking down to the Oder. This canal formed in effect an extension of the ambitious scheme known as the Mittelland Canal connecting the Dortmund-Ems Canal to Berlin. Indeed, the lift was intended to enable boats of 1,000 tons to pass from the Rhine to the Vistula.[5]

After considering various alternatives, it was decided to build a lift just to the west of the uppermost of the existing locks, designed to supplement rather than to replace the locks. An upper canal of lattice girder construction leads to the lift itself, which is of similar construction. On account of the nature of the subsoil, the whole lift rests on a reinforced concrete raft.

The general scheme of the Niederfinow lift is similar to that of the reconstructed Anderton lift, but there is only one trough, and of course, the whole structure is on a far larger scale, being at its opening the largest lift ever constructed. The trough is eighty-five metres long and twelve metres wide, with a depth of water of 2.50 metres. The difference in levels is actually thirty-six metres. The trough is suspended from 128 wire ropes on each side (the large number being intended to minimise danger from breakage) which pass over double channel pulleys 3.5 metres in diameter and are fastened to concrete counterweights arranged in groups of six. To compensate for the weight of the ropes when the trough is at the top, there are chains running from the lower ends of the counterweights to the underside of the trough, exactly counterbalancing the trough and the counterweights. The gates on the trough and the two canal reaches are of the vertically lifting type.

Power for raising and lowering the trough is provided by four electric motors of only seventy-five horse power each, mounted on the trough and connected through pinions to racks on the frame of the lift. The motors were designed to run at exactly the same speed to avoid jamming the trough and were interconnected mechanically so that, in case of the failure of one, the other three could take over the load. The electrical equipment was designed to rely as little as possible on the human element, and the aligning of the water level in the trough with that of the canal was controlled by a photo-electric cell which stopped the motors when the correct level was reached. The operating speed is twelve centimetres per second and a lift takes five minutes, the total time for a complete boat movement from one level to the other being twenty minutes.

The design of the Niederfinow lift was by the Reich Waterways Administration Office at Eberswalde,[6] and a number of contractors were employed. The lift was opened by the Minister of Transport on 21 March

1934. It survived the war and is still at work. The canal, which is in the German Democratic Republic, is now known as the Oder-Havel Canal.

The Federal German Republic's canal authorities started work in 1969 on a lift at Scharnebeck, near Lueneburg, on the new Elbe Lateral Canal, which is to connect the River Elbe at Geesthache (forty kilometres east of Hamburg) with the summit level of the great Mittelland Canal north of Brunswick, enabling traffic to bypass portions of the River Elbe between Geesthache and Magdeburg which are unsatisfactory for navigation at times of low water.[7] The lift is designed with two counterweighted containers, each to accommodate vessels 100 metres long by twelve metres wide, drawing 3.50 metres. These containers are longer than those of the Henrichenburg new lift (ninety metres) and Ronquières incline (eighty-seven metres) so that they can accommodate push-tows, with a vessel 76.50 metres long and a pusher twenty metres long. The container is also 0.50 metres deeper than existing lifts to safeguard the very large barges 11.40 metres wide, by giving an adequate transversal section to allow for a return current to be established in the case of rapid entry or exit. The lift overcomes a rise of thirty-eight metres.

The authority considered a number of alternative plans: a lock with water-saving basins; a transverse inclined plane; a longitudinal inclined plane; and a water slope. Inclined planes were found to be unsatisfactory owing to the varying water levels of the Elbe, about four metres in the bottom reach. The site proved not altogether suitable for a water-slope. The calculations showed that on constructional costs, degree of efficiency and running costs, a double lift with counterweights, broadly similar to the lift at Niederfinow, was far superior to all the other designs considered (allowing for the difference in head of thirty-eight metres), but in respect of maintenance costs, the lock or water-slope would have been superior.

The lift is provided with two towers on either side of each container basin, each carrying two groups of pulleys for fifty-six cables connecting the container with the counterweights. The total weight of the container inclusive of water, reaches 5,600 tonnes and the corresponding counter-weight spread over four times fifty-six cables represents a load of twenty-five tonnes for each cable. Variations in the level of water in the lay-by basins, can be compensated by pumps at the ends of the containers which can either raise or lower the water level in the container. To provide against accidents or power cuts, fixed jacks are provided on which the container will settle down. Two brakes are provided, one an emergency brake which can bring the container to a full stop in five seconds.

The Elbe Lateral Canal is designed to have a rise of a further twenty-three metres at Uelzen, forty-five kilometres south of Lueneburg. The alternatives of a lift similar to Lueneburg or a lock were considered for this site, and a lock was finally chosen. The lift was opened to traffic in 1977.

The other system used in modern German lifts, which has also proved itself in service, originates in the design by Herr Gerdau, chief engineer of Messrs. Haniel & Luegg of Dusseldorf, for a lift at Henrichenburg. This is about fifteen kilometres north of Dortmund, where the Dortmund-Ems Canal encounters a fall from Dortmund of about fourteen kilometres.[8] Herr Gerdau designed a lift consisting of a single trough, sixty-eight metres long by 8.60 metres wide, by 2.5 metres deep, which hung in a cradle carried by five lattice-work supports resting on five cylindrical floats made of steel plate, each 12.8 metres high and 8.3 metres in diameter. These, floating in wells full of water, maintained the whole moving load, estimated at 3,000 tons, in perfect equilibrium. The rise and fall of the trough was controlled entirely by increasing or diminishing the weight of water in the trough, which reversed the equilibrium of the floats and caused them to rise or fall in the wells. The similarity of the plan to the proposals of Messrs. Rowland & Pickering, will be noted.

The motion was controlled by four screw spindles, 26.4 metres high and twenty-five centimetres in diameter, with a bevel wheel at the top driven by bevel gearing and shafts from the high bridge. Lifting gates at each end of the canal reaches and the trough were counterbalanced and could be easily worked by two men if necessary — normally they were worked by electric power, as was the whole installation. Two compound steam engines were originally provided to generate the electricity.

The time needed to effect an actual lift was two-and-a-half minutes, but the movement of a barge from the upper to the lower level, and another in the opposite direction, took twenty-five minutes overall. Estimates of the size of boat with which the lift could deal vary from 600 tons to 950 tons. An official source says 600 – 700 tonnes. Work was started in 1894 and the lift entered service during the winter of 1899-1900. The contractors for the mechanical part of the lift were Messrs. Haniel & Luegg, and for the electrical installation, Messrs. Lahmeyer of Frankfurt.

At first, the authorities appear to have felt uneasy about the first Henrichenburg lift. The necessity of an absolute guarantee of uninterrupted navigation on the Dortmund-Ems Canal led to the construction of an alternative means of passing the change of level at Henrichenburg, and a lock was constructed and entered service in 1917. However in 1962, the continued functioning without serious accident of the original lift had evidently calmed the official fears, and as will be seen, a new and larger installation was built.[9]

During the 1930s, a further lift was constructed in connection with the Mittelland Canal mentioned above. This was at Rothensee near Magdeburg, and connects the Canal, which crosses the Elbe at this point at a high level, with the west bank of the Elbe. It is interesting that although this was under construction in 1934, when the Niederfinow lift was completed, the float system was adopted rather than the counterweight system.[10]

The difference in level (taking medium water in the Elbe) was fifteen metres, but the water level could vary from 10.58 metres at low water to 18.67 metres in time of flood. Like the Niederfinow lift, the Rothensee lift can take 1,000 tonne boats.

The trough, which is borne on two floats only, has a usable length of eighty-five metres, a usable width of twelve metres and a normal water depth of 2.5 metres. The water load is 2,700 tonnes and the total weight to be balanced, 4,800 tonnes. This balancing is effected by the lift of two floats, each ten metres diameter and 2,400 tonnes displacement, which float in water in shafts eleven metres in diameter and fifty-one metres apart on centres. The floats carry frameworks of a height corresponding to the maximum change in level on which the trough rests. There are four lifting motors in the trough bridge, which drive two moveable nuts on each carrier head engaging in guides on the framework of the lift. The trough moves at fifteen centimetres per second. The trough has vertical gates at each end, and the upper canal bay has a vertical gate also: but at the lower end, the lifting gate has to be adjustable in vertical steps of about one metre on account of the variation in the water level in the river of up to 7.5 metres. The sealing between the canal bays and the trough is effected by a rubber belt.

Construction of the lift took years, the sinking of the shafts for the floats being done by the freezing process. The lift was completed in 1939, and is still in operation today: like Niederfinow, it is now in the German Democratic Republic.

In 1928, the decision was taken to modernise the Dortmund-Ems Canal to take 1,000 tonne boats, including the construction of a third means of passing the change of level at Henrichenburg.[11] However, presumably works connected with the Mittelland Canal had priority because it was not until 1955 that the Federal German authorities took up the study of the matter seriously, by which time the size of the vessel to be passed had become the 'European boat' of 1350 tonnes. An additional difficulty was that allowance had to be made for mining subsidence in preparing the design. The upper (Dortmund) level receives no natural water supply so that any water has to be pumped up from the lower level. The trough has a usable length of ninety metres, a width of twelve metres and a depth of three metres, to take boats drawing 2.50 metres and eighty-five metres long. The normal change of level is 13.75 metres, though it can be as much as 14.50 metres.

In this case, the ground conditions were favourable for the sinking of wells for the floats, these being 52.48 metres deep with a diameter of 13.80 metres. In order to ease the strain on the floats as much as possible, both here and at Rothensee, the interior pressure in the floats is higher than atmospheric pressure. The diameter of the floats is ten metres. In this design, there are four guidance towers, two on each side, and the machine room and control room are situated over the trough. The transverse carriers on which the trough rests, and which are in turn mounted on the framework borne by the floats, have at each end nuts which engage on the guides running down the guidance towers. One movement of the trough over 14.50 metres fall, takes 120 seconds, the maximum speed being fifteen centimetres per second. The motors which drive the guides are situated in the top of the guidance towers and are mechanically synchronised by

86

shafting required to work the lift connecting with the base of each guidance tower. Every effort is made by interlocking to eliminate human errors in operating the lift.

The time taken for a boat to enter the lift from the lower canal, to be raised, to leave the lift, and for another to enter the lift, be lowered and leave the lift, should be thirty-four minutes. Assuming a normal working day of sixteen hours, there should be twenty-eight movements each day, and allowing for non-working days, 7,500 movements in a year corresponding to 20.75 million tonnes in weight. In actual operation, one can only count on an annual through-put of fifteen million tonnes, but even this exceeds by at least thirty per cent, the possible through-put of a lock of the type installed in 1917. The arrangements at Henrichenburg therefore, now consist of the old lift at the point where the Dortmund branch of the canal meets the Herne-Munster section almost at right angles, with the lock installed in 1917 to the North, and then even further to the North, the new lift, work on which was completed on 31 August 1962. It was intended to close down the old lift as soon as the new one had proved itself, but although this was done, the old lift was not dismantled while its future was being considered, but it is believed that it will be retained as an industrial monument.[12] It seems surprising that the German authorities should have adopted and continued to construct two very different systems of canal lift, but it seems possible that civil engineering considerations are involved. In any case, both systems have been well tried over many years, and appear to work satisfactorily.

Finally, one may note a reference in a commercial report from the British Embassy at Vienna dated 4 November 1905[13] to a lift then being constructed for testing purposes at Aujezd, which is about three kilometres south east of Prerov (Prerau) in Moravia. This was in connection with the Danube-Oder Canal then projected by the Imperial and Royal Austro-Hungarian Government. This canal has never been constructed but possibly the remains of the canal lift could be found if one went to Aujezd, now in Czechoslovakia. Unfortunately the report, being intended merely as commercial intelligence, throws no light on the nature of the intended lift.

A list of lifts given in a modern guide to the Rothensee life includes this lift, stating that it was finished and had a lift of 36 metres.

THE FUTURE

Had this been written in 1950 only a born optimist would have predicted a rosy future for the subject of this book. No incline had been constructed on any canal since the Foxton incline at the turn of the century; and while the German authorities had built two large lifts during the period between the wars, no other canal undertakers appeared to be enthusiastic about them, and future development showed every sign of being along the lines of high-rise locks.

Thirty-five years later, the picture seems quite different. Several large inclines and lifts have been put in as part of the up-grading of the canal system of Europe, and an entirely new and sophisticated device, the water slope, has made its appearance in a full scale experiment. The advantages of the systems of changing levels which have been described in this work, the saving of water and, perhaps as important in the modern world, of time, associated with both inclines and lifts have been widely recognised in Western Europe, and no doubt further installations will be made in the course of improving the canal network of the continent. It is sad that at present, the improvements of the English canal system, which it is claimed could be carried out at far less cost then the building of motorways, still show little prospect of getting official approval; but sooner or later, commercial use must return to English waterways, and when rebuilding takes place, no doubt the use of inclines or lifts in suitable places will return to the country which can claim to have pioneered it.

PLATES

1. The Incline at Overtoom near Amsterdam, a relic of the earliest type of incline which survived until the late nineteenth century.

Dr Ir. M. Goppel

2. The Incline at Lizzafusina near Venice possibly installed in the late fifteenth century.

91

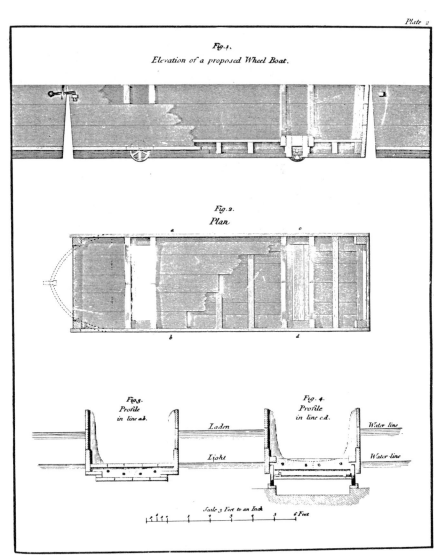

Plate 2

Fig. 1.

Elevation of a proposed Wheel Boat.

Fig. 2.

Plan

Fig. 3.
Profile
in line ab.

Fig. 4.
Profile
in line cd.

Laden

Water line

Light

Water line

Scale 3 Feet to an Inch

6 Feet

3. A contemporary drawing of the type of wheeled boat which worked on the Bude Canal.

4.   The top of the Rolle Canal incline. It is thought that a waterwheel in a pit at the top of the incline drove an endless chain by means of a vertical shaft engeging in cogs in the overhead wheel at the top. Boats were attached to the endless chain by a short length of chain at one end of the incline and cast off again at the other.

Bideford Public Library

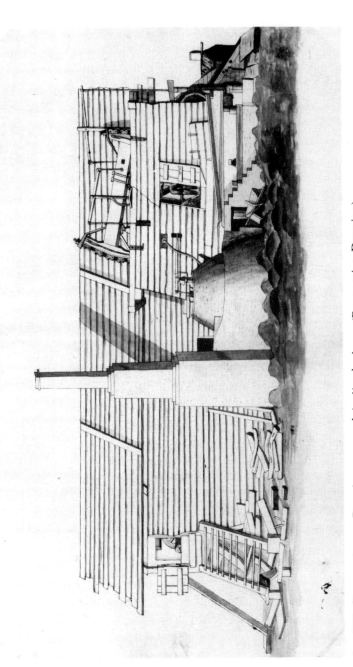

5. Winding engine at Donnington wood inclined plane, (Perspective Drawing).

by William Minor, 28 September 1793

Newcomen Society

6. The Hay Incline at Coalport apparently in working order. The top of the cradle can be seen at the bottom of the right hand track, with the cable running up the track to the top.

Credit. Ironbridge Gorge Museum.

7. Shrewsbury Canal – Trench inclined plane.

Good Words magazine 1899 W. Howard Williams

8. Shrewsbury Canal – Trench incline c. 1910.

BWB W. Howard Williams

9. The only known photograph of the Georgetown Incline on the Chesapeake and Ohio Canal, apparently taken while under construction.

Canal Press Inc.

10. A maintenance boat at the summit of Plane 9 West, Morris Canal U.S.A. The two cradles and hinged boat eased the problem of passing a boat over the brow of an incline into the upper level of the canal.

Canal Press Inc.

11. The only known illustration of the Dartmouth inclined plane on the Shubenacadie Canal, Nova Scotia. One rail can just be seen on the right.

Dartmouth Heritage Museum

12. A pleasure boat in its cradle at one of the inclines on Kanal Elblaski formerly known as the Oberland Canal.

Mrs A.M.C. Switek

13. A view of the incline taken from a boat ascending an incline on Kanal Elblaski.

Mrs. A.M.C. Switek

14. The water wheel for working one of the Inclines on the Elblag Canal.

Mrs Switek

15. A contemporary drawing of the carriage and caisson on the Blackhill Inclined plane, Monkland Canal. Mitchell Library, Glasgow

16. At Orange Street Newark N.J. the Morris Canal originally went under a railroad, but the railroad was lowered five feet and an electrically operated incline fitted up. The canal water passed from one side of the railroad to the other by an inverted siphon.

17. The original "Marine Railway" at Swift Rapids, Trent Canal, Canada. Now replaced.

Ontario Department of Industry & Tourism

18.   BRUSSELS – CHARLEROI CANAL. Ronquieres Incline. The foot of the incline with one of the tanks. Note the carrying wheels of the tank. Each wheel is independently sprung.

Photo by J.H. Boyes

19. Aerial view of the incline at St Louis d'Arzviller, Canal de la Marne au Rhin.
Compagnie Francaise d'Entreprise

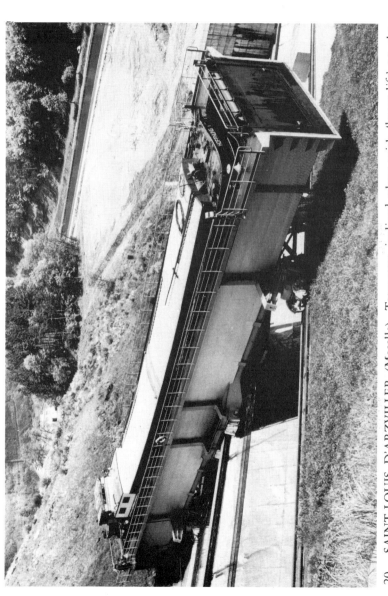

20. SAINT-LOUIS D'ARZVILLER (Moselle). Transverse inclined plane with 'barge-lift' on the Marne-Rhine Canal in the Zorn Valley.

Compagnie Francaise d'Entreprise

21. A boat being propelled up the water slope at Montech, France: the shield is lowered to keep the boat afloat while it travels up the slope.

photo: J.H Boyes

22. The lower end of the water slope at Montech, France, showing the shield which pushes the boats up the slope raised.

photo: J.H. Boyes

23. Preparing to lower a compartment boat into the River, Stanley Ferry Aire & Calder Navigation.

Messrs Wilson's Wakefield

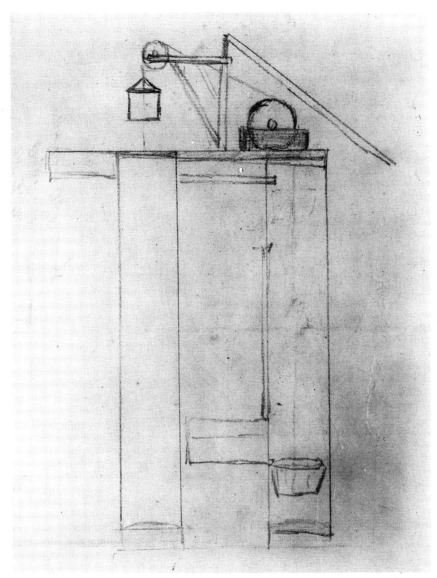

24. A sketch of the crane for trans-shipping cargoes Donnington Wood Canal Shropshire.

Newcomen Society

25. The Anderton Lift, River Weaver Navigation, about 1944 after conversion to electric operation.

Dr. T.P.C. Mulholland

26. *Canal du Centre, Belgium* A boat emerging from No 3 lift, The hydraulic ram supporting the left hand tank can be clearly seen.

photo: the late Frank Lawson

27. *Canal du Centre, Belgium.* A view of the control cabin on No 4 lift. The present four lifts are to be replaced by one large left.

photo: the late Frank Lawson

28. Trent Canal, Ontario, Canada; The Lift Lock at Kirkfield with the two lock chambers in the 'up' and 'down' position; the water level above the lock is that of Balsam Lake, 841 ft. above M.S.L., the summit water level on the canal.

Department of Transport, Canada

29. The monolithic construction of the Scharnebeck lift, Elbe Lateral Canal, Federal Republic of Germany.

photo: J.H. Boyes

30. The impressive lift at Scharnebeck near Lueneberg on the Elbe Lateral Canal, Federal Republic of Germany.

photo: J.H. Boyes

31. The new lift at Henrichenburg, Dortmund-Ems Canal, Federal Republic of Germany. View from the top of the lift with the lower canal level in the left background.

photo: J.H. Boyes

ACKNOWLEDGEMENTS

My thanks are due to many who have helped and encouraged me, and firstly to Mr. Charles Hadfield, for encouraging me to undertake this work, and for much helpful advice and criticism.

To the Librarians and staff of Rutland County Library and Leicester County Library for obtaining many out of the way books and articles for me, the National Library of Wales and the Swansea Public Library, the Cambridge University Library, the Science Museum Library and the British Library for allowing me to consult books in their collections, and the Llanelli Public Library for providing a translation of a work in Welsh.

To many members of the Newcomen Society and the Railway & Canal Historical Society for advice and help; in particular to the late Dr. H.W. Dickinson, the late Mr. E.A. Forward, Mr. D. Crabtree, Mr. Charles E. Lee, Mr. H. Robinson, the late Mr. L.T.C. Rolt, Mr. Richard Dean, Mr. C.H.A. Townley, Mr. J.G.B. Hills, Mr. F. Doerflinger, Mr. P.A. Stephens, Mr. K.R. Clew, Mr. P.G. Rattenbury and Mr. John Boyes.

To Jean and Genevieve Lavault, Dr. Michel Goppel, Mr. Derek Stoyel, Mr. John Alves, Mr. Robert S. Mayo, Mr. Harry L. Rinker, Dr. Robert F. Legget, Mr. T.J. Ryan, Mrs. Enid Mallory and members of the American Canal Society for information and assistance in my enquiries into foreign canals.

Especially to the late Mr. W. Howard Williams for his advice and help over many years in the study of Shropshire canals.

To many other people who have helped me, and particularly Mr. Christopher Marsh, Dr. Christopher Tuplin, Dr. Melvin Kranzberg and Dr. Bulferetti, Mr. Michael Handford and Dr. Hugh Torrens for sending me his article on the Somersetshire Coal Canal caisson lock.

And finally, I must express my gratitude to my predecessors in this field and especially to William Chapman and M. J.J. Hirsch.

NOTES

Notes to Chapter I (pp. 1–4)

1. Jean Vercoutter 'Excavations at Mirgissa II' *Kush (Journal of the Sudan Antiquities Service)* Vol XIII (1965) pp 68–9.
2. Charles E. Lee 'Some Railway Facts and Fallacies' p.2. *Trans. Newcomen Society* Vol. XXXIII (1960-61). Dr. Christopher Tuplin suggests that in Corinth ancient things of uncertain date tended to be ascribed to Periander.
3. J.Needham 'China and the Invention of the Pound Lock' passim. *Trans. Newcomen Society* Vol. XXXVI (1963-64).
4. *The Book of Ser Marco Polo the Venetian* ed. H. Cordier trans. Sir H. Yule (1903) Vol. ii p.175 n.2.
5. J. Barrow, *Travels in China* (1804) p.152.
6. G.B. Cressey, *China's Geographical Foundations* (1934) fig.138.
7. J.J. Hirsch, *Notice sur les Elevateurs et Plans Inclinés pour Canaux* (1881) pp.21-2.
8. Reproduced in R. Thelu 'Les Elevateurs a bateaux sur plan incliné p.67 *Revue de la Navigation Interieure et Rhenane* 1966 No. 3.
9. Brewster's *Edinburgh Encyclopaedia* Vol. XV (1830) pp.220 and 298. John Smeaton, *Diary of a Journal to the Low Countries 1755* (1938) mentions seeing a similar incline.
10. Quoted in *Technology & Culture* (Oct. 1978) Vol 19 No. 4 p.719.
11. M. Chevallier *Histoire et description des voies de communication aux Etats Unies* (1840) Vol. 1 p.392.
12. V. Zonca *Nuovo Theatro dei machine et edificii* (1621) pp.58-60 and J. Leupold. *Theatrum Machinarum Hydro-Technicarum* (1724) pp.179-180 & Plate XLVIII.
13. W.B. Parsons *Engineers and Engineering in the Renaissance* (1939) pp.374-5.
14. e.g. N. Grollier de Serviere, *Receuil d'ouvrages curieux de mathematique et de mechanique* (1719)

Notes to Chapter II (pp. 5–9)

1. The Knight of Glin, 'The Architecture of Davis Duckart' *Country Life* 28 September 1967 and 5 October 1967.
2. W.A. McCutcheon, *The Canals of the North of Ireland* (1965) pp.62-77.
3. W. Chapman *Observations on the various systems of Canal Navigation* (1797) p.6 gives the rise as 60 feet.
4. *Reports of the late John Smeaton* (1812) Vol. II p.178.
5. For a discussion of Jessop's possible influence on this. C. Hadfield and A.W. Skempton, *William Jessop, Engineer* (1979) pp.17-18.
6. A. Rees *Cyclopaedia* (1819) art 'Canal'
7. See G. Taylor and A. Skinner *Maps of the Roads of Ireland* 2nd. edition (1783 reprinted 1969)
8. A. Young *A Tour in Ireland* (Dublin 1780) Vol. II p.91.
9. See *Dictionary of National Biography* under Richard Reynolds.
10. A. Raistrick *Dynasty of Ironfounders* (1953) p.189.

11. J. Plymley, *General View of the Agriculture of Shropshire* (1803) pp.290-9 report by T. Telford.
12. W. Howard Williams. 'Canal Inclined Planes of East Shropshire' *Journal of Industrial Archaeology* Vol. 2 No. 3 (1965) pp.91-105. I am greatly indebted to the late Mr. Howard Williams and the late Mr. E.A. Forward for information on the inclines of Shropshire generally.
13. Telford records that a fully loaded boat would raise a boat one third loaded.
14. Chapman p.5.
15. Plymley p.291.
16. Chapman. errata sheet.
17. R.L. Tonkinson *Inclined Planes on the Shropshire Canals* (1964) p.54.
18. *Trans. Newcomen Society* vol II Drawing No. 44. These drawings are in the Science Museum Library.
19. C. Hadfield *The Canals of the West Midlands* (1966) pp.40-41.
20. F. Mullineaux, 'The Duke of Bridgewater's Underground Canals at Worsley' *Transactions of the Lancashire & Cheshire Antiquarian Society* Vol. 71 (1961) pp.152 et seq. *also* E.R. Hassall & J.P. Trickett, 'The Duke of Bridgewater's Underground Canals' *The Mining Engineer* October 1963 pp.45-54.
21. Hon. & Rev. F.H. Egerton: 'Underground Inclined Plane made at Walkden Moor by the Duke of Bridgewater' *Journal of Society of Arts* 18 (1800) pp.265 et seq.
22. Earl of Ellesmere *Essays contributed to the Quarterly Review* (1853) Essay VII p.243. But according to J. Hirsch p.14, the French traveller Dupin found it still at work in 1826.
23. D. Owen *Canals to Manchester* (1978) p.50.
24. Hon. & Rev. F.H. Egerton *A Letter to the Parisians and the French Nation upon Inland Navigation* (1818) p.47.
25. I am indebted to Mr. Charles Hadfield for information about Benjamin Sothern.

Notes to Chapter III (pp. 10–23)

1. Helen Harris and Monica Ellis *The Bude Canal* (1972) gives a full account of this extraordinary undertaking.
2. Acts L and P 14 G.III c. 53.
3. For John Edyvean, see pp. 53–4.
4. 2nd. ed. 1791.
5. C. Hadfield *Canals of South West England* (1967) p.144.
6. For Fulton's life see H.W. Dickinson, *Robert Fulton Engineer and Artist* (1912).
7. Patent No. 1988.
8. R. Fulton *Treatise on the Improvement of Canal Navigation* ch. V.
9. C. Hadfield p.175.
10. R. Thelu p.68.
11. E.M. Gauthey *Memoires sur les Canaux de Navigation* (1816) p.406 et seq.
12. See also J.J. Hirsch, pp. 16–17.
13. For Green's career, see C. Hadfield, 'James Green as Canal Engineer' *Journal of Transport History* I no.1 (1953)
14. Harris & Ellis p.26.
15. At that date the use of steam locomotives was not considered.
16. Acts L and P 59 G.III c. 55.
17. The following description is founded on Harris and Ellis ch. 3.
18. Harris and Ellis p.80.
19. C. Hadfield *Canals of South West England* p.138.
20. *Industrial Archaeology* 7 No. 1 (Feb 1970) pp.75-84.
21. C. Hadfield p.141.
22. For this account of the Grand Western Canal I am indebted to H. Harris *The Grand Western Canal* (1973).

23. For Provis' report on Wellisford incline see Harris pp.104–109.

24. *Taunton Courier* 4 July 1838.

25. C. Hadfield, private information.

26. C. Hadfield *Canals of South West England* p.66.

27. For the history of the Chard Canal, see *The Chard Canal* published Chard History Group.(1972 2nd. ed.)

28. *Minutes of Proceedings Inst. Civil Engineers* XIII (1853-4) p.213 in the discussion on James Leslie's paper on the Blackhill Incline.

29. *Sherborne Journal* 5 August 1841.

30. P. Smith *Waterways Heritage* (2nd. ed. 1972) p.49.

31. P.M.N. Wilson, 'Early Water Turbines in the United Kingdom' p.228 *Trans. Newcomen Society* Vol. XXXI (1957-9)

32. C. Hadfield p.70.

33. C. Hadfield *Canals of South Wales and the Border* (2nd. ed. 1967) p.39. The rises are calculated by C. Hadfield from the Railway Deposited Plan of 1865. In Green's report they are given as: 52′ 6″, 53′ 11″ and 85′.

34. Ap Huw *Hanes Dyffryn Gwendraeth gan Hanesydd y Cynoesau* (1873) ch. 2.

35. R.G. Thomas 'Pembrey Parish, Early Industrial Efforts' *Trans. Carmarthenshire Antiquarian Society 20 (1926-27) p.49.*

36. *Colliery Guardian* (1867) p.286.

37. C. Hadfield p.39.

38. C. Hadfield p.40.

39. R.L. Tonkinson *Inclined Planes on the Shropshire Canals* (1964) p.54 et seq. The account of these inclines is chiefly drawn from this monograph.

40. Private correspondence.

41. W. Howard Williams *Industrial Archaeology* 2 No. 3 pp.96-7.

42. C. von Oeynhausen and H. von Dechen *Railways in England 1826 and 1827* (1971) p.73.

43. R.L. Tonkinson p.63.

44. *Trans. Newcomen Society* vol. II Drawing No. 98.

45. C. von Oeynhausen and H. von Dechen p.74.

46. John Randall *History of Madeley* (1880) p.94.

47. C. Hadfield *Canals of West Midlands* (1966) p.238.

48. H.G. Archer 'The Romance of Inland Navigation' *Good Deeds* (1899) But H.R. de Salis *Bradshaw's Canals and Navigable Rivers of England and Wales* (2nd. ed. 1918) p.12, says it went out of use in 1902.

49. D. Crabtree, private information.

50. C. Hadfield p.238.

51. W. Howard Williams *Industrial Archaeology* 2 No. 3 pp. 101–2.

52. For this incline, see W. Howard Williams pp. 102–3.

53. C. von Oeynhausen and H. von Dechen pp.70-72.

54. C. Hadfield *Canals of South West England* pp.131-2.

Notes to Chapter IV (pp. 24–40)

1. J. Leslie, 'Inclined Plane for Canal boats' discussion p.209 *Minutes of Proceedings Inst. Civil Engineers* XIII (1853-4).

2. C. Hadfield, private information.

3. T. Dwight *Travels in New England and New York* (1823, reprinted 1969) Vol. I pp.234-6.

4. For a short bibliography see *American Canals* No. 20 (February 1977) p.7.

5. H. Skramstad 'The Georgetown Canal Incline' *Technology and Culture* Vol. 10 No. 4 (1969) deals with this incline in detail.

6. W.S. Sanderlin *The Great National Project* (1946) Curiously, the incline is barely mentioned in this detailed full length history of the Chesapeake and Ohio Canal.

7. T.F. Hahn & O.W. Crowder *Towpath Guide to the Chesapeake and Ohio Canal* (1971) p.20.

8. For information on the Beauval incline I have relied on M.A. Mallett 'Plan Incline pour

transbordement des bateaux à Beauval près Meaux' *Memoires et Compte-rendu des Travaux de la Societe des Ingenieures Civiles* 1 (1892) p.627 et seq.

9. Préfecture de la Seine, service des Canaux. private correspondence 20 October 1950.
10. C. Hadfield *Canals of South Wales and the Border* (2nd. edition 1967) p.78.
11. C.C. Vermeule, 'The Morris Canal' *Trans. Newcomen Society Vol XV (1934-5)*.
12. *Biographical Dictionary of American Civil Engineers* (1972).
13. C.P. Yoder *Delaware Canal Journal* (1972) pp.97-8.
14. D. Stevenson *Sketch of the Civil Engineering of North America* (1838) pp.206 et seq.
15. C.P. Yoder 'The High Climbing Morris Canal' *Canal Currents* No. 15 (1971).
16. *Technology and Culture* 15 No. 1 (1974) p.108.
17. C.C. Vermeule p.201.
18. I am indebted for details of the Morris Canal system to James Lee *The Morris Canal* (2nd. edition 1974) Mr. Lee aims to restore the entire plane and machinery of Plane No. 9 West.
19. E.H. Keating 'The Shubenacadie Canal' *Trans. American Society of Civil Engineers* CCLXVII (1883) I am indebted to Mr. Charles Hadfield for drawing my attention to this canal, and to Mr. Robert Legget for permitting me to read his discussion paper *Two Early Canadian Marine Railways* (1975).
20. His report describes only two inclines, at Dartmouth and Portobello.
21. A first hand account of the canal as originally built is by Schmid 'Der Elbing-Oberlandische Canal' in *Zeitschrift fur Bauwesen* (1861) pp.150-156 with plates. See also J.J. Hirsch p.32. et seq and *Government Bluebooks* (1895) CII No. 345 (Miscellaneous reports commercial) 'Report on Inland Waterways of Germany' (1894) pp.6-7.
22. C. Hadfield, private information. See J.J. Hirsch, plate II.
23. The dimensions are given by Schmid in *fuss* and *zoll*. One *fuss* equalled 1.029728 feet unless Schmid was using Rhenish *fuss* which equalled 1.3 feet.
24. Polish Inland Waterways Board, private correspondence, 1967.
25. The Polish Authorities call it 'a historical curiosity'.
26. My account is based on S. Tanabe 'The Lake Biwa-Kioto Canal' *Minutes of Proceedings Inst. Civil Engineers* 117 (1893-4) pp.353-359 and Wm. E. Trout III 'A True Account of the Adventures of an American on Japan's Biwako Canal . . . .' *The Towpath Post* (1974) Vol. 4 pp.2-11, an excellent if whimsical eye witness description of the canal.
27. J. Leslie, C.E. 'Description of an Inclined Plane. . . . constructed in 1850' *Trans. Royal Scottish Society of Arts* VI (1856) p.69 et seq. (the paper was actually read in 1851) and also 'Inclined Plane for canal boats' *Minutes of Proc. Inst.Civil Engineers* XIII (1853-4) pp.205 et seq.
28. E.A. Pratt *Scottish Canals and Waterways* (1922) p.157.
29. This account is mainly based on *Engineering* 25 January 1901 p.111-114. I am also indebted to Mr. R.K. Gardner for his views given in a talk to the East Midlands area of the Railway and Canal Historical Society.
30. P.A. Stevens *The Leicester Line* (1972) p.167.
31. A.H. Faulkner *The Grand Junction Canal* (1972) p.193 and Plate p.173.
32. P.A. Stevens p.178.
33. S. Tanabe 'The Lake Biwa-Kioto Canal' *Scientific American* 75 (1896) pp.341 and 345-6.
34. S. Tanabe, *Biwako Sosui.*
35. Wm. E. Trout III. p.7.
36. James Lee *The Morris Canal* (2nd. edition 1974) pp.84-5.
37. To quote the Department of Transport's *Trent Canal System* (1949).
38. Correspondence from Mr. J. Ryan, superintending engineer, Trent Canal. (1950).
39. Department of Transport *Navigation Canals* (1959).
40. Correspondence from Mrs. Enid Mallory, Peterborough, Ontario (1963).
41. D.L. Walton 'Visit to "Big Chute" Marine Railway' *American Canals* bulletin No. 4 (February 1973) There was also a level crossing at Plane 12 East, Newark N.J. on the Morris Canal. See J. Lee, p.87.
42. W.E. Keenan, 'New 100-ton Marine Railway on the Severn-Trent Waterway' *American Canals* No. 32 (February 1980).
43. *Invention Bulletin* No. 197 pp.30–31.

Notes to Chapter V (pp. 41–46)

1. The Ministry of Public Works and Transport.
2. J.J. Hirsch, p.84.
3. G. Willems 'Le Rachat de la Chute de Ronquières sur le canal de Charleroi a Bruxelles' *in Revue de la Navigation Interieur et Rhenane* 10 May 1961 pp.352 et seq.
4. The most accessible account of the incline is A. Gallez *The sloping lock of Ronquières* published Tourist Federation of Hainault, 8th. Edition 1968.
5. G. Willems & others. 'Le Plan Incline de Ronquières' in *Proceedings of the 21st. International Navigation Congress* (1965) S1 – 2 pp.57-97.
6. D. Edwards-May *The French Waterway Connection* (1978).
7. M. Marchal and M. Tiphine, 'Le Plan Incline d'Arzviller' in *Revue de la Navigation Interieure et Rhenane* 25 September 1964 p.666 et seq.
8. M.R. Vadot and others 'The Transversal Inclined Plane on the St. Louis-Arzviller Canal from the Marne to the Rhine' *Proceedings of the International Navigation Congress Bulletin* (1971) Vol. III No. 9 pp.57–81.
9. M. Marchal and M. Tiphine, p.673.
10. 'Le Franchissement des hautes chutes: La Solution Pente d'eau' *Revue de la Navigation Interieure et Rhenane* 25 September 1961 pp.685 et seq. A similar idea was put forward by the American Oliver Evans about 1806. *American Canals* No. 24 (February 1978).
11. F. Klapper 'Navigating the Heights' *The Dock and Harbour Authority* January 1973.
12. *Encyclopaedia Britannica* 13th. edition art 'Yenisei'. According to the latest edition, art 'Yenisey River' the incline was under construction in 1971.
13. N.A. Semanov and V.I. Vovkushevsky 'High Pressure Navigable Constructions' *Proc. 21st. International Navigation Congress* (1965) S 1-2 pp.227-229.
14. C. Marsh, private correspondence. *Invention Bulletin* No. 197 p.30.
15. or 156 wheels and 78 carriers *Invention Bulletin* p.30.

Notes to Chapter VI (pp.47–52)

1. K.W. Williams *Trans. Newcomen Society* Vol. XXVIII (1951-2) p.56.
2. 'English Place Name Elements' (1956) Part I pp.134-5.
3. E. Ekwall, *Concise Oxford Dictionary of English Place-Names* 4th. Edition (1960) p.151. But the Editors of *Place Names of Nottinghamshire* (1941) are uneasy about this.
4. S. Runciman *Fall of Constantinople* 1453 (1965) pp.105–6.
5. E. Bradford *The Great Siege, Malta 1565* (1961) pp.148-149.
6. M. Baumgardner and F.G. Hoenstine *The Alleghany Old Portage Railroad 1834-1854* (1952).
7. S. Welch *Report on the Alleghany Portage Railroad* (1833 reprinted 1973).
8. Quoted in W.H. Shank *The Amazing Pennsylvania Canals* (1965) pp.35-6 from an unnamed source.
9. W.H. Shank pp.30-35.
10. B. Roberts, private information.
11. C. Hadfield *Canals of Yorkshire and North-East England* Vol. 2 (1973) p.367 et seq.
12. D.D. Gladwin *The Canals of Britain* fig 22 shows this process at the top of the illustration.
13. R. Pilkington, *Small Boat through Sweden* (1961) pp. 49–52.
14. H. Skramstad 'Georgetown Canal incline' pp.558-9.
15. *Encyclopaedia Britannica* 13th. edition art 'Tehuantepec'.
16. C.E. Lee article in *Railway Magazine* May 1939 pp.365-7.

Notes to Chapter VII (pp. 53–58)

1. C. Hadfield *Canals of South West England* (1967) p.165.
2. C. Hadfield pp.165-7.
3. *The Monthly Review* (1791) pp.119-120 quoted by Hadfield.
4. Rees *Cyclopaedia* art 'Canal'.
5. C. Hadfield *Canals of West Midlands* (1966) p.157.
6. A. Raistrick *Dynasty of Ironfounders* (1970) pp.215-6.
7. B. Trinder *The Industrial Revolution in Shropshire* (1973) p.137.
8. J. Dutens *Memoirs sur les Travaux Publiques d'Angleterre.*
9. C. Hadfield, *Canals of North West England* (1970) Vol. 1 p.132.
10. C. Hadfield Vol. 1 p.131 et seq.
11. C. Hadfield, Vol. 2 p.381.
12. R. Hansford Worth 'Early Western Railroads' *Annual Report and Trans. Plymouth Institution* 10 (1887-90) pp.79-81. And see C. Hedges *The Tavistock Canal* (1975).
13. C. von Oeynhausen and H. von Dechen p.72.
14. C. Hadfield *Canals of South West England* p.129.
15. R. Hansford Worth.
16. C. von Oeynhausen and H. von Dechen pp.67-8.
17. This is likely to have been the incline from Bathampton Quarries to the Kennett and Avon Canal. see Sir A. Elton, 'The Pre-History of Railways' *Somersetshire Archaeological and Natural History Society* (1963) pp.55-6.
18. C. Hadfield, *Canals of North West England* Vol. 12 pp.308-312.
19. K.R. Clew *The Somersetshire Coal Canal and Railways* (1970) ch. 3.
20. K.R. Clew p.48.
21. K.R. Clew p.51.
22. K.R. Clew, *Kennet and Avon Canal* (2nd. edition 1973) p.65.

Notes to Chapter VIII (pp. 59–61)

1. M. Handford *The Stroudwater Canal* Vol. 1 (1976) pp.60-75. Bridge's patent was no. 720 of 1758.
2. A. Young *A Six Month's Tour through the North of England* (1771 reprinted 1967) pp.200 et seq.
3. P.K. Roberts, 'Terminal tunnels of Central Manchester' *Journal of the Railway and Canal Historical Society* XXVI No. 2 (1980) pp.54-58.
4. W.A. McCutcheon *Canals of the North of Ireland* (1965) p.69.
5. *Trans. Lancashire and Cheshire Antiquarian Society* 75-6 (1965-66) pp.226-8.
6. C. Hadfield *Canals of West Midlands* p.41.
7. C. Hadfield p.157.
8. A. Raistrick *Dynasty of Ironfounders* p.188.
9. J. Plymley *Agriculture of Shropshire* pp.294-5.

Notes to Chapter IX (pp. 62–71)

1. O. Haubold 'Ein Schiffshebewerk' *Zeitschrift des Vereines deutscher Ingenieure* 78 (1934) p.1434.
2. No doubt named in honour of the Elector (later King) of Saxony, Frederick Augustus 'the just' 1750-1827.
3. Patent No. 1892.
4. *Sherborne Mercury* 13 October 1794.
5. To whom I am indebted for all this information.

6. I have relied on K.R. Clew *The Somersetshire Coal Canal and Railways* (1970) ch. 2 for this account.
7. H. Torrens 'The Somersetshire Coal Canal Caisson Lock' *Journal of Bristol Industrial Archaeological Society* 8 pp.4–10.
8. Report by Professor Dr. Ing. A. Rohnisch pp.36–48 *Proceedings of the 21st. International Navigation Congress* (1965) S 1–2.
9. Patent No. 1981.
10. Information from Mr. H. Robinson.
11. W. Chapman, p.10.
12. C. Hadfield *Canals of West Midlands* p.174.
13. I am indebted to the late L.T.C. Rolt and Messrs. H. Robinson and R. Dean for their views on this very interesting problem.
14. R. Thelu pp.70–71.
15. F. Gauthey pp.406–8.
16. Patents No. 2912 and 3324.
17. Edward Smith *A Description of a Patent Perpendicular Lift erected on the Worcester and Birmingham Canal near Tardebig . . .* (1810).
18. C. Hadfield *Canals of West Midlands* pp.141–2.
19. Patent No. 2284.
20. K.R. Clew *Dorset and Somerset Canal* ch. 4.
21. The 'impression' of the lift in K.R. Clew's book shows the frame over, not under, the caisson, which seems a more workable arrangement.
22. Patent No. 3670.
23. H. Spencer *London's Canal* (1961) pp.42, 46–7, 49–50.

Notes to Chapter X (pp. 72–74)

1. In this account I have drawn on James Green's 'Description of the Perpendicular Lifts for passing boats from one level of canal to another, as erected on the Grand Western Canal' *Trans. Inst. Civil Engineers* 2 (1838) p.185 et seq. and on H. Harris *The Grand Western Canal* (1973) passim.
2. J. Green p.190.
3. Acts L and P 27 and 28 Vic c. 184.

Notes to Chapter XI (pp. 75–80)

1. See *Dictionary of National Biography* 1st. Supplement under Latimer Clark.
2. C. Hadfield *Canals of North West England* Vol. 2 pp.383–4.
3. Acts L and P. 35 and 36 Vic c 98.
4. See S. Duer 'Hydraulic Canal Lift at Anderton' *Minutes of Proc. Inst. Civil Engineers* XLV (1875–6) pp.107 et seq.
5. J.A. Saner 'A Short Description of the River Weaver Navigation' *Journal of the Royal Society of Arts* (1888) p.820–1.
6. S. Duer, discussion.
7. J.A. Saner 'Reconstruction of the Canal-boat lift on the River Weaver at Anderton' *Minutes of the Proc. Inst. Civil Engineers* CLXXX (1909–10) p.239 et seq.
8. 'Ascenseur Hydraulique des Fontinettes' *Le Genie Civil* VI No. 7 (November 1888) pp.101–103.
9. Ch. Freson *Notice sur les Ascenseurs Hydrauliques pour Bateaux* (1888) p.22.
10. L.F. Vernon-Harcourt 'Some Canal River and other Works in France, Belgium and Germany' *Minutes of Proc. Inst. Civil Engineers* XCVI (1888–9) pt. II pp.182–4.
11. *Royal Commission on Canals* (1906–1909) Vol. VI pp.11 and 97.
12. L.F. Vernon-Harcourt *Rivers and Canals* (2nd. edition 1896) p.404.

13. from the Regional Director of Navigation, Lille.
14. A. Desoutter and P. Hanotte *Arques/les Fontinettes — l'ascenseur à bateaux, notice technique* (1979).
15. L.F. Vernon-Harcourt 'Some Canal, River and other Works' pp.184-6 and Plate 6.
16. C. Freson, pp.26 et seq.
17. A. Gallez *The Sloping Lock of Ronquières* pp.11-17, describes the lifts with illustrations.
18. L.F. Vernon-Harcourt *Rivers and Canals* p.408.
19. C. Castan *Histoire de la Louvière* (1931) pt. 2 p.71.
20. L. van Wetter and L.G. Schoentjes report in *Proc. 13th International Congress of Navigation* section 1-2.
21. D. Edwards-May *The French Waterway Connection* (1978) pp.4-5.
22. Correspondence from T.J. Ryan, superintending engineer Trent Canal, 1950.

Notes to Chapter XII (pp. 81–87)

1. J.A. Saner 'Reconstruction of the Anderton Lift' *Minutes of Proc. Inst. Civil Engineers* CLXXX (1909-10) pp.239 et seq.
2. C. Hadfield *Canals of North West England* Vol. 2 p.390.
3. M. Ingham 'Anderton Face Lift' *Waterways News* April 1974 and May 1974.
4. *Waterways News* No. 115 (November 1981) p.8.
5. Articles in *Engineering* Vol. 137 (1934) pp.374-6 and 141 (1936) pp.444-5.
6. Where an exhaustive booklet *Das Schiffshebewerk Niederfinow* was published in 1934.
7. J. Illiger: 'Structures for dealing with large differences in head for the Lateral Canal of the Elbe in the German Federal Republic' *Proc. International Navigation Congress Bulletin* No. 10 pp.23-45.
8. L.F. Vernon-Harcourt 'Henrichenburg Lift, Dortmund-Ems Canal' *Minutes of Proc. Inst. Civil Engineers* CLII (1902-3) p.215. The dimensions have been taken from *Die Absteigs-bauwerke Henrichenburg* n.d.
9. H.G. Braun and others 'Le Nouvel ascenseur pour bateaux d'Henrichenburg a Waltrop' report in *Proc. 2lst. International Navigation Congress* S 1-2 pp.3-16.
10. W. Reinhardt 'The Rothensee Barge Elevator' *Engineering Progress* 15 No. 12 (December 1934) pp.211-3.
11. Official publication *Die Absteigsbauwerke Henrichenburg* n.d.
12. Information from Mr. C. Marsh. It is interesting to note that in 1982, a further deep lock was being considered owing to the increased traffic.
13. Government Bluebooks CXXL (1906).

INDEX

131

134

Wells, L.B. 76
Werrington, Devon 12
Whitelaw & Stirrat, Messrs 16
Widemouth, Cornwall 10
Wilkinson, J. 17
Willems, G. 42
Williams, Major C. 49
Williams, E. Leader 55, 75–76
Williams, H. 17
Windmill Incline, Stirchley 17–20
Wombridge, Salop 21

Woodhouse, J. 67–68, 81
Worcester & Birmingham Canal 67–69
Worsley, Lancs 8, 60
Wrantage, Som. 15–16

Yenisei, River 45, 94
Ypres 2
Yser, River 2
Yule & Wilkie, Messrs 36

Zafosina 3